CAMBRIDGE ANTI
RECORDS SOC

VOLUME 7

LADY FRANCES SIDNEY, COUNTESS OF SUSSEX,
attributed to Steven van der Meulen (181)

CATALOGUE
OF THE PORTRAITS IN
CHRIST'S, CLARE AND
SIDNEY SUSSEX COLLEGES

BY
J. W. GOODISON M.A.
Emeritus Fellow of Darwin College, Cambridge

CAMBRIDGE
1985

© Cambridge Antiquarian Records Society
ISBN: 0 904323 07 2

Set in IBM Press Roman by Margaret Helps & Associates, Norwich
Printed and bound in Great Britain by
The Witley Press, Hunstanton, Norfolk

CONTENTS

GENERAL EDITOR'S NOTE

This volume has been published with the help of generous grants from Christ's College, Clare College and Sidney Sussex College. The society is also grateful to the author and to Mr. John Mitchell of Christ's College for their assistance in providing photographs of portraits and to the Bursars of Clare College and Sidney Sussex College for their cooperation in having photographs made. Plates I, II, III, V, VI, VIII (Fisher), IX, X, XI and XII are by Christopher Hurst.

The biographical notes have been contributed by Mr. John Mitchell (Christ's), Dr. J. D. Pickles (Clare) and Mr. T. S. Wyatt (Sidney Sussex), and the society owes each of them a debt of gratitude for this. Necessarily the notes are brief and vary to some extent in treatment; however it is hoped that the limited details given and the inclusion of references to Venn's *Alumni* and certain other standard works will satisfy demands for biographical information.

LIST OF PLATES

ABBREVIATIONS
AND SELECT REFERENCES

Atkinson and Clark	T. D. Atkinson and J. W. Clark, *Cambridge described and illustrated,* 1897
C.A.S.	Cambridge Antiquarian Society, catalogues of the First and of the Second Exhibition of University and College Portraits, 1884 and 1885
D.N.B.	*Dictionary of National Biography*
Goodison	J. W. Goodison, *Catalogue of Cambridge portraits: I. The University collection,* 1955
Masters	*A Catalogue of the Several Pictures in the Public Library and Respective Colleges in the University of Cambridge . . . By a Gentleman of the University,* n.d. Published about 1790, and generally attributed to the authorship of the Rev. Robert Masters, but more probably by the Rev. Thomas Kerrich.
N.C.B.E.L.	*New Cambridge Bibliography of English Literature*
Peile	John Peile, *Biographical Register of Christ's College 1505–1905,* 2 vols., 1910–13
Venn	J. and J.A. Venn, *Alumni Cantabrigienses,* 10 vols. in 2 parts, 1920–54

A.R.A.	Associate of the Royal Academy
bt.	Bought
cat.	Catalogue
coll.	Collection (of)
exh., exbn.	Exhibited, exhibition
hon.	Honourable, honorary
K.C.	King's Counsel
kt.	Knight or knighted
P.R.A.	President of the Royal Academy
P.R.S.A.	President of the Royal Scottish Academy
R.A.	Royal Academy, Royal Academician
rep.	Reproduced (in)

In the dimensions, which are sight measurements, height precedes width; 'right' and 'left' refer to the point of view of the spectator, unless otherwise indicated.

PREFACE

The first consideration in cataloguing these portraits has been to verify the accepted identification of their subjects, which has proved to be, on the whole, reliable. Directly involved in this has been the establishment, as far as possible, of the history of each portrait, which includes the question of how it originated and why, which in turn leads to its relation to an *ad vivum* standard of portraiture. The solution of these problems has frequently been far from complete, owing to the sheer absence of information, but in these cases what can be ascertained has been recorded.

The catalogues cover paintings, drawings, sculpture and a few figures in painted glass. Factual information has been obtained from a variety of sources, to which reference will be found in the notes to each entry. Thanks are due to many correspondents and others for the trouble and courtesy with which enquiries have been met. Valuable also has been the material in the archives of the National Portrait Gallery, freely placed at my disposal over a number of years. A particular debt must be gratefully acknowledged to Mr. T. S. Wyatt of Sidney Sussex College, whose unstinting help has uniquely facilitated my work on the portraits of this College.

J. W. Goodison

INTRODUCTION

Any attempt to piece together some account of the formation of these three collections of portraits is severely limited by the scarcity of information already mentioned in the Preface. The first lists are contained in a small pamphlet, 'By a gentleman of the University', to quote the title-page, published about 1790, of somewhat uncertain authorship but referred to in these pages as *Masters* (see p. viii). The lists enumerate only fourteen portraits for Christ's College, eight for Clare College (if two miniatures are excluded), and thirteen for Sidney Sussex College. Indications of how and when these few portraits arrived are absent, and research has largely failed to make this good. Sidney Sussex College has an advantage of its own over these lists, in a series of inventories drawn up at the entry into office of each Master, beginning in 1639.

Following on after *Masters*, but making no additions, is a series of lists in C. H. Hartshorne, *The book rarities in the University of Cambridge* (1829), pp. 478–516. The last published lists are those in T. D. Atkinson and J. W. Clark, *Cambridge described and illustrated* (1897), indicating additions at the most about doubling the number of portraits in *Masters* and Hartshorne. This is still modest in comparison with numbers today: Christ's College 102, Clare College 40, Sidney Sussex College 54.

Of an original intention to compile catalogues of the portraits in all the Cambridge colleges, these three alone have been realisable owing to other demands, in completed form. A catalogue of the portraits in the various departments, libraries, etc., of the University, which took priority over this undertaking, was published in 1955 (see p. viii).

CHRIST'S COLLEGE

Earliest of the portraits belonging to the College are five late medieval royal portraits in the windows of the Chapel (nos. **24–25, 41–43**), which are associated with the refounding of God's House as Christ's College by the Lady Margaret Beaufort in 1506. Only another nine are recorded by the end of the eighteenth century (*Masters*, p. 28), including the fine whole-length of the Foundress in the Hall (no. **71**), first known of as in the possession of the College in 1714. Of the remaining eight, the origins of only two, both acquired by benefaction in the eighteenth century, are known (nos. **14, 50**), three are without provenance (nos. **6, 66, 72**), and three are now missing, including a drawing by David Loggan, 1684, of Ralph Cudworth, Master from 1654 to 1688.

Portraits of Masters of the College reach back, with a few gaps, into the seventeenth century, though the earliest, of Samuel Bolton (no. **6**), is rather doubtful. Among other portraits, the sculptural head of Milton by Edward Pierce (no. **54**) and the portraits of Charles Darwin (nos. **16–19**) are in a class which makes a unique claim to attention. Leaving aside more recent portraits, three are by painters of recognised eminence, two of the seventeenth century, of Sir Thomas Baines by Isaac Fuller (no. **2**) and of Sir John Finch by Sir Peter Lely (no. **26**), and one of the eighteenth century, of Laurence Echard by Sir Godfrey Kneller (no. **23**).

Among a few other portraits now missing, one may be mentioned, a small drawing by Robert White of John Sharp, Archbishop of York, bought in 1883. Omitted from the catalogue are the nineteenth-century statue of the Foundress over the Gateway, and the glass portraits in the east window of the Chapel by Sir William Nicholson.

AUSTEN-CARTMELL, JAMES

1862–1921. Son of James Cartmell, Master 1849–81. Admitted 1881, B.A. 1884. Called to the Bar 1889; became 'Treasury Devil', *i.e.* Junior Equity Counsel to the Treasury. [*Peile*, ii, 675; *Venn*, II.i, 530].

1   Painter unknown

$32\frac{1}{8}$ × $28\frac{1}{8}$ in. (81.6 × 71.4 cm.). Canvas. Bust, turned half left, facing quarter left, looking front. Bare-headed; clean-shaven. Wears dark dress with lace jabot.

Given by his sister, 1922.[a]

NOTE. (a) College Meeting, 31 July 1922, minute 5. The name of the sister is not specified; he was the only son in a family of four.

BAINES, SIR THOMAS

*c.*1624–1681. Son of a yeoman of Whaddon (Cambs). Admitted 1638, B.A. 1642/3. Remembered for friendship with Sir John Finch with whom he graduated; became M.D., a Fellow of the College of Physicians and a member of Padua University. Together they signed the petition to Charles II for the formation of the Royal Society. When Finch was knighted he procured the same honour for Baines. [*D.N.B.*; *Peile*, i, 455; *Venn*, I.i, 114].

2   By ISAAC FULLER   PLATE IV

$27\frac{3}{4}$ × $21\frac{3}{4}$ in. (70.5 × 55.2 cm.). Canvas. Half-length, turned and facing half left, looking front. Bare-headed, dark brown hair to shoulders; clean-shaven. Wears loose brown robe over white shirt tied at the neck with a black ribbon. Inscribed lower left, 'Sir Thomas Baines'.

Given by George F. Rose, 1947.[a] Coll. Finch family, Burley-on-the-Hill, Leicestershire (formerly Rutland); descended to Major James Hanbury; his sale, Christie's, 20 June 1947 (25).

Sir Thomas Baines was the lifelong friend and companion of Sir John Finch, whose nephew Daniel Finch, Earl of Winchilsea and Earl of Nottingham, built Burley-on-the-Hill where this portrait and that by Lely of Sir John Finch (see no.26) remained until the sale of 1947. In 1649 the two friends proceeded to the degree of M.A., and it seems a not improbable guess that the two portraits are connected with this event, a possibility which accords very well with their apparent ages. The portraits can, in any case, hardly be later than October 1651, when the two set out for France and Italy, though circumstances compelled them to return in 1652 before leaving finally again in 1653, when they remained in Italy until 1661.

REPRODUCED. A. Malloch, *Finch and Baines* (1917), p. 32; *Connoisseur*, cxl (1957), 232.

NOTE. (a) College Meeting, 4 October 1947, minute 12. The gift was made to commemorate the centenary of the tenancy of a College property by Mr. Roe's family firm.

3   By JOSEPH CATTERNS

$24 \times 19\frac{1}{2}$ in. (60.9 × 49.5 cm.), oval. Marble relief. Bust, turned, facing and looking quarter left. Bare-headed, hair curling to the shoulders; clean-shaven. The bust draped.

Given by Daniel, second Earl of Nottingham, c. 1684.

This medallion, with one of Sir John Finch, forms part of a monument erected to the memory of the two friends in Christ's College Chapel by Finch's nephew, Daniel, Earl of Nottingham (later also Earl of Winchilsea). The monument was not finished before Michaelmas 1684.[a] The two friends are buried together in the same vault near the monument, the only known work of Joseph Catterns, signed lower left, 'Josephus Catterns/Londinensis/Sculpsit'. The two medallions are taken from portraits by Carlo Dolci, formerly at Burley-on-the-Hill, painted in Florence between 1665 and 1670 when Finch was Envoy and Resident at the Court of the Grand Duke of Tuscany, accompanied by Baines.[b]

REPRODUCED. K. A. Esdaile, *English church monuments* (1946), p. 99, fig. 111 (the whole monument).

NOTES. (a) R. Willis and J. W. Clark, *The architectural history of the University of Cambridge* (1886), ii, 209. (b) Now in the Fitzwilliam Museum, Cambridge. They are mentioned by F. Baldinucci, *Notizie de' professori del disegno*, vi (1728), 503, where Baines is called 'Dr. Fava'; as 'fava' is the Italian for 'beans', this suggests how the name was then pronounced (catalogue of 'Italian art and Britain', R.A. exhibition, 1960, p. 19, no. 10).

BARKER, JOHN

c. 1727–1808. Admitted 1745, B.A. 1748/9, D.D. (by royal mandate) 1781, Fellow 1749. Held various College offices, including Praelector & Dean, from 1755, and several curacies and livings. Master 1780–1808. Vice-Chancellor 1780–81. [*Peile*, ii, 247; *Venn*, I.i, 86].

4   By SILVESTER HARDING

$4\frac{5}{8} \times 3\frac{1}{2}$ in. (11.6 × 8.8 cm.), oval. Water-colour. Turned, facing and looking three-quarters right. Bare-headed, white cauliflower wig; clean-shaven. Over black dress with bands, wears black academical gown with scarf.

Source of acquisition unknown.[a] Coll. Sir Busick Harwood, M.D., F.R.S. (1745(?)–1814).[b]

As he wears the black scarf of a Doctor of Divinity, the portrait cannot be before 1781, the date at which he took this degree, though as Harding's recorded visits to Cambridge range from 1788 to 1799 it is probably some years later. These small portraits painted for Sir Busick Harwood appear to have been done from the life (see note a). A repetition is in the Fitzwilliam Museum (no. 622[g]).

NOTES. (a) Already in the College by 1913, since it is mentioned in *Peile*. Possibly given by J. W. Clark, who gave seven similar portraits by Harding from Sir Busick Harwood's collection to the Fitzwilliam Museum in 1903 (see *Goodison*, p. 85, no. 118). See also nos. **21** and **45**. (b) Professor of Anatomy and Downing Professor of Medicine, Cambridge. He had a large number of portraits of contemporary members of the University executed for him in this form by Harding. See F. R. Owst, '*Iconomania* in eighteenth-century Cambridge', in *Proceedings of the Cambridge Antiquarian Society*, xlii (1949), 68–72.

BARKER, JOSEPH

*c.*1820–1901. Admitted 1840, B.A. 1844. Curate of Berkeswell with Barston (Warwicks.), 1845–67; vicar of Eardisland (Herefs.), 1867–1901. [*Peile*, ii, 468; *Venn*, II.i, 152].

5   By CANON G. F. WESTON
$5\frac{1}{4}$ × 4 in. (13.3 × 10.1 cm.). Pencil. To knees, seated, turned, facing and looking half right, right hand raised to his chin, left arm by his side. Bare-headed; clean-shaven. Dress only slightly indicated.

Given by Mrs. C. W. Benson, daughter of Canon Weston, 1923.[a]

Probably drawn by Canon Weston while an undergraduate at Christ's College, 1840-44. See also nos. **33, 34, 40, 48, 51, 69, 79, 93, 94, 96, 100**.

NOTE. (a) College Meeting, 15 March 1923, minute 12.

(?) BOLTON, SAMUEL

1606-1654. Admitted 1625, B.A. 1628/9, D.D. 1650. For a decade minister of important London churches; an able preacher. Master of Christ's 1646-54. Vice-Chancellor 1651-2. [*D.N.B.; Peile*, i, 368; *Venn*, I.i, 176].

6   Painter unknown
$29\frac{3}{8}$ × $24\frac{3}{8}$ in. (74.6 × 61.9 cm.). Half-length, turned and facing slightly right, looking front. Wears close black cap over white cap; white moustache and pointed beard. Black dress with plain white turned-over collar and white cuffs. Holds partly open before him in his right hand a gold-tooled book with gilt edges.

Source of acquisition unknown. Exh. C.A.S., 1884 (158).[a]

Masters, p. 28, lists in the Master's Lodge a portrait of Samuel Bolton (1606-1654), Master of Christ's College 1645-54, and one of an unknown man. When exhibited in 1884 it was described as 'Unknown', but there seems no doubt that it is this portrait which is the one listed by Atkinson and Clark in 1897 (whose list includes no 'Unknown') as of Samuel Bolton. Engravings of Bolton[b] show a similarly bearded man in the same kind of attire, though the beard is dark. The features in the painting, which is of very mediocre quality, give so little individual character as to provide no basis for a satisfactory comparison with the engravings, though they are not inconsistent with those which are there shown. If this is Bolton no portrait in the possession of the College can now be identified with Masters's 'Unknown', and the identification as Bolton thus remains uncertain. A suggestion that this may represent

John More (d. 1592) can be rejected on grounds of date and by comparison with the engraved portrait of him in Henry Holland's *Herωologia* of 1620 (no. **59**).

NOTES. (a) As 'Unknown'. (b) E.g. by W. Faithorne, prefixed to Bolton's *The dead saint speaking to saints and sinners living: in several treatises* (1657); see L. Fagan, *The engraved works of William Faithorne* (1888), p. 23.

BROUGHTON, HUGH

1549–1612. B.A. (Magdalene) 1569/70. Fellow of St. John's 1570; Fellow of Christ's 1572–78; Prebendary of Durham 1578, losing fellowship through Durham preferment despite a ruling by Dr. Perne, Vice-Chancellor, and patronage of Sir Walter Mildmay. No Cambridge connection after 1580. A Puritan controversialist and a Hebrew scholar, unpopular for his 'extreme opinionativeness' (Fuller). [*D.N.B.; Peile,* i, 94; *Venn,* I.i, 231].

7   Painter unknown, 1588

$33\frac{1}{4} \times 27\frac{1}{4}$ in. (84.5 × 69.2 cm.). Wood. Three-quarter length standing, turned and looking front, facing quarter left, holding an open book in his left hand and yellow gloves in his right. Wears black gown over black dress, with a white ruff and plain white cuffs. Inscribed upper left, ' הֶבֶל אֵי – AM ·· 5517[a] ANNO DNĪ ·', and upper right, '1588 · AETATIS · SVAE · 37'. Below the inscription left, his coat of arms;[b] below that at right, four books standing on a shelf.

Given by Allen Cotton Borrett, 1957, in memory of his son Major Allen James Borrett (d. 1944).

1588 is the date of Broughton's first published work, *A concent of Scripture*, in which he attempted to settle scriptural chronology. The engraving of 1620 by John Payne (see below), which corresponds with this portrait, was used as the frontispiece to John Lightfoot's edition of Broughton's collected works (*The works . . . of Mr. Hugh Broughton*), 1662.

ENGRAVED. Line-engraving by John Payne, 1620.[c]

NOTES. (a) "Where is Abel? – Anno mundi 5517". The inscription comes from Genesis iv. 9; the date, which is original and undamaged, is the equivalent of Anno domini 1757, and must be a mistake for A.M.5347, i.e. A.D. September 1587 – September 1588. (b) Sable, between three owls argent a chevron argent differenced with a crescent gules (for a second son). (c) This corresponds exactly with the present picture, from which it is presumably taken.

BUCHANAN, JOHN YOUNG

1844–1925. Admitted 1889; Hon. M.A. 1891. A man of much wealth, well connected abroad. Scientist and geographer of some note, maintaining private laboratories in Edinburgh and London. Lived in Hobson Street, in a house later part of Christ's, and bequeathed silver for use in the Master's Lodge. [*Peile*, ii, 889; *Venn*, II.i, 429].

8   By J. P. L. TINAYRE, 1909

$35\frac{7}{8}$ × 28 in. (91.1 × 71.1 cm.). Canvas. Three-quarter length standing, turned, facing and looking nearly half right, the right arm resting on the back of a chair, the left hand in his trouser pocket. Bare-headed, dark hair; dark grey moustache. Wears grey jacket and trousers over red waistcoat, with gold watch-chain. Holds a cap in his right hand, an umbrella hooked over his left wrist. Signed and dated lower left, 'LOUIS TINAYRE. PARIS 1909'.

Source of acquisition unknown, perhaps bequeathed 1925.

BUTLER, JACOB

1681–1765. Admitted 1698, B.A. 1702/3. Barrister. Owned an estate at Barn-well, Cambridge, becoming known as 'The Squire of Barnwell'. Eccentric and quarrelsome, setting up as champion of public rights. An unsuccessful candidate for parliament as 'An Old Briton'. [*Peile*, ii, 144; *Venn*, I.i, 272].

9   Painter unknown

$7\frac{1}{2}$ × $5\frac{7}{8}$ in. (19.0 × 14.9 cm.). Oils behind glass. Half-length, turned, facing and looking profile left. Wears black three-cornered shovel hat over bushy grey hair; clean-shaven. Black dress with long bands. Inscribed on the wooden backing, 'Jacob Butler Esq$^{\underline{re}}$/1765'.

Given by the Rev. I. Frank Buxton (of Oxford), 1934.[a]

From the technique this appears to be probably of late nineteenth-century date. It goes back to an etching of Butler in *Bibliotheca Topographica Britannica*, ed. J. Nichols, v (1790), no. XXXVIII, opposite p. 1 of the Appendix. A drawing by M. Tyson from the etching is in the Fitzwilliam Museum (see *Goodison*, p. 79, no. 108).

NOTE. (a) College Meeting, 6 October 1934, minute 20. A label at the back of the painting gives the name of the donor and states that it was in the first place offered to the Fitzwilliam Museum.

CARRINGTON, EDMUND ALFRED

1892–1916. Admitted 1911. Joined the Navy as a rating in 1914; later commissioned in the Wiltshire Regiment and killed in action.

10   Artist unknown

$20\frac{1}{8}$ × $18\frac{1}{8}$ in. (51.1 × 46.0 cm.). Pencil. Whole-length seated in an armchair, turned, facing and looking half left, writing in a book held on his knees, the left leg crossed over the right. Bare-headed; clean-shaven. Wears naval rating's uniform.

Source of acquisition unknown.[a] *Missing, 1983.*

NOTE. (a) A pencil inscription on the back, '24/6/16', may possibly indicate the date when the drawing was received by the College. A second drawing of Carrington, a head in crayon, formerly in the Master's Lodge, cannot now be traced (see College Meeting, 26 May 1936, minute 9).

CARTMELL, JAMES

1810–1881. B.A. (Emmanuel) 1833, S.T.P. 1849, Fellow of Christ's 1833, Dean 1835, Tutor 1839, Master 1849–81. Reformed college finances and did much important building work, including rebuilding Hall. Vice-Chancellor 1849, 1865, 1866. Buried in ante-chapel. [*Peile*, ii, 436; *Venn*, II.i, 530].

11   By T. C. WAGEMAN, 1848

$14\frac{1}{8} \times 10\frac{3}{8}$ in. (35.9 × 26.3 cm.). Water-colour. To below knees, seated in an upholstered armchair, turned half left, facing slightly left, looking front, holding papers on his lap with his right hand, his left grasping his right wrist. Bare-headed, dark brown hair; clean-shaven but for brown side-whiskers. Wears dark grey jacket, waistcoat and trousers, with high collar, and white stock tied in a bow. In background left, books on a table. Signed and dated lower right, 'Wageman/July [?] 1848'.

Source of acquisition unknown.[a]

NOTE. (a) Already in the College by 1913, since it is mentioned in *Peile*.

CLARK, JOSEPH

c.1815–1894. Admitted 1834, B.A. 1838. Fellow 1839–54. Rector of Kegworth (Leics.), 1853–93. [*Peile*, ii, 452; *Venn*, II.ii, 44].

12   By TREVOR HADDON

$9\frac{1}{2} \times 6\frac{5}{8}$ in. (24.1 × 16.8 cm.). Indian ink, red chalk and pencil. Bust, turned, facing and looking three-quarters left. Bare-headed, dark hair; clean-shaven. Wears dark double-breasted jacket buttoned across, with high stiff collar. Signed left, 'TREVOR HADDON'.

Source of acquisition unknown.

The costume is of about 1850–60, which agrees with the apparent age of the sitter. Haddon was working in Cambridge in the 1930s, so this drawing must be based on another, contemporary portrait, now unknown.

COVEL, JOHN

1638–1722. Admitted 1654, B.A. 1657/8, D.D. 1679, Fellow 1659, Master 1688–1722. Vice-Chancellor 1688–9, 1708–9. Travelled extensively, writing copious journals. Chaplain to Levant Company, meeting Sir John Finch (*q.v.*); Chaplain to William of Orange in Holland, 1682, but dismissed for reporting William's tyrannical treatment of his wife. William, as King, met Covel as Vice-Chancellor but did not snub him, observing that he 'could distinguish between Dr. Covel and the Vice-Chancellor'. Organised partly at his own expense, the 'beautification' of the College Chapel, 1702 and 1722 (clock and bell his gift). An amateur botanist, architect and collector. Buried in ante-chapel. [*D.N.B.*; *Peile*, i, 559; *Venn*, I.i, 406].

13   By CLAUDE GUYNIER, 1716

$28\frac{3}{8} \times 24\frac{1}{4}$ in. (72.1 × 62.2 cm.). Canvas. Half-length, turned half right, facing slightly right, looking front. Bare-headed, light wig; clean-shaven. Wears scarlet robe opening down the front, with white fur tippet and bands. Inscribed upper left, 'DR COVEL'. Inscribed on the back of the canvas (re-lined), 'C Lauduis Guynier pinxit 1716'.

Source of acquisition unknown. Coll. Edward Harley, second Earl of Oxford, at Wimpole Hall, Cambridgeshire; his sale, London, Lock, 8 March 1742 (8), bt. Wilson (for 15/-); in the possession of the College by 1897.[a]

He is shown in the special robe formerly worn at Congregations, etc., by Doctors of Divinity, Law and Physic;[b] Covel became a D.D. in 1679. Guynier's receipt for this portrait, which he painted for the Earl of Oxford when Lord Harley, is at Welbeck Abbey, dated 22 March 1716; he charged £3. 4s. 6d. for it. It may be that it was painted when he was working at Wimpole, where he is known to have been later in 1716.[c]

NOTES. (a) *Atkinson and Clark,* p. 414. (b) J. R. Tanner, *The historical register of the University of Cambridge* (1917), p. 194. (c) R. W. Goulding and C. K. Adams, *Catalogue of the pictures . . . at Welbeck Abbey* (1936), p. 447.

14   By VALENTINE RITZ

$29\frac{3}{8} \times 24\frac{3}{4}$ in. (74.6 × 61.9 cm.). Canvas. Half-length, turned slightly left, facing and looking slightly right. Bare-headed, grey periwig; clean-shaven. Wears scarlet robe lined with white fur, opening down the front, with white fur tippet and bands. Within a painted oval.

Given by William Cole, before 1749.[a] *Masters* p. 28, no. 1.

Cole says of this portrait, 'By accident I lit on a Picture of *Dr. Covel* in his *Scarlet close Congregational Robes* and *Ermine Hood*, which, as they had none of him in the *College*, I gave to the *Master's Lodge*, where it now hangs: He appears to be a jolly *well-looking Man* of an *open Countenance*, and by People's Account that well remember very like him: it is but an *ordinary Picture*, done by one *Valentine Ritz* a *German Painter* who had been established at *Cambridge* for a vast number of years, where he died *6 or 7 years since.*'[b] For the robe he wears, see above, no. **13**. When old.

NOTES. (a) British Library, Add. MS. 5821 (Cole's 'Various collections for Cambridgeshire', vol.XX). The fly leaf, fol. 2, is dated 1747–48, but the portion relating to Christ's College is dated at the beginning on fol. 47, 'Apr 14, 1749'. (b) *Ibid.* note a, fol. 77.

CREWE, SIR RANULPHE

1558–1646. Admitted 1576. Barrister. M.P. 1597. Purchased Manor of Crewe (Ches.), ancient family home, and built Crewe Hall. Speaker of House of Commons 1614, knighted after dissolution. Serjeant-at-Law 1615. Involved in trial of Overbury's murderers. Lord Chief Justice 1624/5. Removed from office by Charles I, 1626, for refusing to affirm legality of forced loans. Benefactor. [*D.N.B.*; *Peile*, i, 136; *Venn*, I.i, 418].

15   Painter unknown

49 × 39 in. (124.5 × 99.0 cm.). Three-quarter length, seated, a book in his

left hand, which hangs by his side, his right elbow resting on a masonry pedestal, the hand in front. Wears a round black cap with a white lace edging. Long black robe, with a white ruff. Grey moustache and close beard. To right and behind the figure a red curtain, to left a masonry column on a pedestal. Upper left, in cursive lettering, 'Sr Randal Crewe'.

Given by the Rev. Geoffrey Mather, 1977. Sold by the Trustees of the Crewe Estate, Christie's, 9 December 1955 (76), bt. Mather.

Much damaged, perhaps in the fire in 1866 at Crewe Hall, which he built, and repainted. As he is in the dress of a private gentleman, and not in legal robes, presumably to be dated after his dismissal from the King's Bench in 1626, which is not contradicted by his apparent age. The donor was directly descended from Sir Ranulphe, and was the purchaser at Christie's in 1955.

DARWIN, CHARLES ROBERT

1809–1882. Admitted 1827, after studying at Edinburgh. B.A. 1832, Hon. LL.D. 1877. Naturalist on the voyage of H.M.S. Beagle 1831–6. Lived in Cambridge 1836–7, while putting the collection from this voyage in order and collating results; at this time treated as a Fellow-commoner at Christ's. Internationally famous after publication of *The Origin of Species*, 1859, and *The Descent of Man*, 1871. Settled at Down (Kent) in 1842, where he lived a life of incessant study. [*D.N.B.; Peile*, ii, 428; *Venn*, II.ii, 228; *N.C.B.E.L.*, iii, 1364–8].

16   By JAMES TISSOT, 1871   PLATE IX

$12\frac{1}{2} \times 7\frac{3}{4}$ in. (31.7 × 19.7 cm.). Water-colour, pencil and lithographic outline. Whole-length, seated on a hassock in a small armchair, turned, facing and looking half right, leaning forward with his arms folded in his lap, the right leg crossed over the left. Bare-headed, bald; long white beard and white moustache; in the act of laughing. Wears brown jacket, grey trousers, black shoes and pink socks. The wood-framed chair is upholstered in green, and has a fringed white antimacassar over the back; brown hassock.

Source of acquisition unknown. Anon. sale (= D. Mitford), Christie's, 5–8 March 1912 (first day, lot 197), bt. C. Davis.

The Christie sale of 1912 consisted of the original drawings for the portraits in chromo-lithography which appeared in *Vanity Fair* from January 1869 to March 1889. Lot 197 is catalogued as 'Darwin (Charles), "Natural Selection", September 30, 1871. J. Tissot. (Lithograph)'. A prefatory note to the catalogue reads, 'N.B. Sixteen of the drawings by Tissot were partly drawn in outline by him on lithographic stone in black; one copy of each was then printed, and that copy was completed and coloured by Tissot. Attention is drawn to these in the Catalogue. The dates are those of the numbers of "Vanity Fair" in which the various drawings were reproduced in chromo-lithography.'

REPRODUCED. *Vanity Fair*, 30 September 1871 ('Men of the Day. No.33').

17   By W. W. OULESS, R.A.

$23\frac{3}{8} \times 21\frac{1}{2}$ in. (59.4 × 54.6 cm.). Canvas. Half-length, turned, facing and looking nearly profile left. Bare-headed, bald; long grey hair, bushy grey beard and moustache; brown complexion. Wears dark jacket and waistcoat. Signed and dated lower left, 'W. W. Ouless / 1883 / replica'.

Source of acquisition unknown; already in the College in 1897.[a]

This replica by Ouless repeats his original portrait of Darwin, painted for his son W. E. Darwin and signed and dated 1875, now on loan to Darwin College from George Darwin. Of it Darwin, in a letter to Sir Joseph Hooker, wrote, 'I look a very venerable, acute, melancholy old dog; whether I really look so I do not know.'[b] Though Darwin and others were inclined to consider the portrait by Collier belonging to the Linnean Society as the best one of him, his son Sir Francis Darwin considered it 'not so simple or strong a representation of him as that given by Mr. Ouless'.[c]

ENGRAVED. Etching by P. Rajon.

NOTES. (a) *Atkinson and Clark*, p. 414.   (b) Francis Darwin, *Charles Darwin* (2nd edition, 1902), p. 292. (c) *Ibid.*

18   By HORACE MONTFORD

Relief plaque, $18\frac{1}{2} \times 15\frac{1}{8}$ in. (46.9 × 38.4 cm.), oval, of irregular outline. Bronze. Head, turned, facing and looking half right, revealing a little of his right shoulder. Bare-headed, bald, long hair; moustache and long beard; heavy eyebrows.

Source of acquisition unknown.

One of a number of sculptured portraits of Darwin by Montford.

19   By WILLIAM COUPER

Bust, $39\frac{3}{4}$ in. high (including pedestal $7\frac{1}{2}$ in. high; 101.0 cm., pedestal 9.0 cm.). Bronze. Turned and facing front, looking slightly right. Bare-headed, bald; moustache and long beard. Wears jacket and double-breasted waistcoat. Inscribed on pedestal, 'DARWIN'. Signed on the cut-off left, 'W$\underline{^m}$ Couper / N.Y.'.

Given by the American Delegates to the Darwin Commemoration, 1909.[a] Exh. Cambridge, Darwin Centenary Exhibition, 1909 (119).

The bust was commissioned from Couper by the New York Academy of Sciences, and a bronze cast of it was presented by the Academy to the American Museum of Natural History, New York, in 1909 at a celebration to mark the hundredth anniversary of Darwin's birth and the fiftieth anniversary of the publication of *The origin of species*. In 1960 the bust was returned to the New York Academy of Sciences, where it now is. Two casts were made in plaster, besides the cast in bronze at Christ's College.

NOTE. (a) *Christ's College Magazine*, xxiv (1909–10), 15. The presentation was made by Professor H. F. Osborne.

DARWIN, SIR FRANCIS

1848–1925. Third son of Charles. B.A. (Trinity) 1870; M.B., M.A. 1875; Sc.D. 1909. Studied medicine at St. George's Hospital, but did not practise. Assisted his father in work at Down until his death, then settled in Cambridge. Reader in Botany 1888–1904. F.R.S. 1882. President of British Association 1908–9; Hon. Fellow of Christ's 1906. [*D.N.B. 1922-30; Peile*, ii, 746; *Venn*, II.ii, 228].

20   By SIR WILLIAM ROTHENSTEIN

$35\frac{1}{2} \times 27\frac{5}{8}$ in. (90.1 × 70.2 cm.). Canvas. Half-length seated, turned, facing and looking nearly profile left. Bare-headed, dark hair; dark beard and moustache. Wears brown cloak over grey suit. Signed and dated lower right, 'W.R./ Repl. 1906'.

Given by his family, 1925.[a]

This is a replica by Rothenstein of an original of 1905, which is in the Botany School, Cambridge.[b] The head corresponds with a drawing by Rothenstein dated 1903 in the possession of Mr. C. F. Cornford, Cambridge.

NOTES. (a) Given after his death, see *Christ's College Magazine*, xxxiv (1924-6), 186. (b) *Goodison*, p. 60.

DAYRELL, MARMADUKE

1770–1821. Admitted Fellow-Commoner 1789–90; the last of five members of the family at Christ's; succeeded his father as squire of Shudy Camps (Cambs.), 1790. [*Peile*, ii, 328; *Venn*, II.ii, 261].

21   By SILVESTER HARDING

$4\frac{1}{8} \times 3\frac{1}{4}$ in. (10.4 × 8.2 cm.), oval. Water-colour. Turned, facing and looking profile right. Bare-headed, white wig; clean-shaven. Over dark blue coat with yellow waistcoat, and choker and jabot, wears black and gold fellow-commoner's gown. When young.

Source of acquisition unknown.[a] Coll. Sir Busick Harwood, M.D., F.R.S. (1745(?)-1814).

A repetition is in the Fitzwilliam Museum (no. 622[b]).

NOTE. (a) Already in the College by 1913, since it is mentioned in *Peile*. See also nos. **4** and **45**.

DOWNS, BRIAN WESTERDALE

1893–1984. Admitted 1912; B.A. 1915. Lecturer in Modern Languages and English 1918. Fellow 1919, Tutor 1928, Master 1950–63. Vice-Chancellor 1955–57; Professor of Scandinavian Studies 1950–60. Writings chiefly on Norwegian literature. [*Who's Who*].

22   By PHYLLIS DODD,[a] 1957

$29\frac{5}{8} \times 24\frac{1}{2}$ in. (75.2 × 62.2 cm.). Canvas. Half-length seated, turned and facing slightly right, looking front, hands crossed in his lap. Bare-headed, grey hair; clean-shaven; spectacles. Wears black academical gown over black cassock, with white bow tie and bands. Background a design of College heraldic emblems (the antelopes, eaglet, portcullis and rose of the Foundress, Lady Margaret Beaufort) in green and yellow grey. Signed upper left, 'P. DODD'.

Commissioned by the College 1956, and painted 1957.

He is shown attired as Vice-Chancellor of the University. A repetition of the portrait, copied from this painting in 1958, belonged to the sitter. Considered a good likeness.

NOTE. (a) Mrs. Phyllis Bliss.

ECHARD (or EACHARD), LAURENCE

1670–1730. Admitted 1687, B.A. 1691/2. Related to contemporary Master of St. Catharine's; resided in Christ's 1688–96, probably compiling material for future literary work. Held a series of livings in Lincolnshire while producing a great mass of books on geography and history, notably *A Compendium of Geography*, 1691, and *History of England*, 1707. [*D.N.B.; Peile*, ii, 109; *Venn*, I.ii, 80].

23   By SIR G. KNELLER   PLATE VIII

35 × 27 in. (74.9 × 68.6 cm.). Canvas. Turned nearly half right, facing quarter right, looking front, a manuscript book, which he holds with his left hand and on which he places his right, open on a table before him at right. Bare-headed, light curled wig; clean-shaven. Wears black gown with bands. Formerly inscribed on the back, 'Laurence Echard/S.ʳ G. Kneller'.

Given by a number of senior members of the College, 1905.ᵃ Coll. R. R. Cross, Liverpool.

Re-lined.

ENGRAVED. Line-engraving by G. Vertue, 1719, as after Kneller, frontispiece to Echard's *History of England*, ed. 1720.

NOTE. (a) Accepted College Meeting 23 May 1905, minute 3; see also *Christ's College Magazine*, xix, 99.

EDWARD THE CONFESSOR

c. 1005–1066. King of the English 1043–1066.
[*D.N.B.*; biography by F. Barlow, 1970].

24   Artist unknown

Painting on glass, 32 × 17 in. (81.2 × 43.2 cm.). Half-length standing, turned, facing and looking front, the head inclined to his left. Crowned and haloed, long golden hair; slight chin beard. Wears red mantle with an ermine cape over a white robe, a sceptre in his left hand, a ring held up in his right. Behind the head is a view of an interior with windows and red pillars, behind the body is a golden hanging.

This and four other portraits on glass (see nos. **25, 41–43**) are in the windows of the College Chapel. They divide into two series, one with figures of a larger size consisting of this and a portrait of Henry VI (no. **41**), and the other with figures of a smaller size consisting of portraits of Henry VI, Henry VII and Queen Elizabeth of York (nos. **25, 42, 43**). The two larger figures date from the early part of the reign of Henry VII (1485–1509) and are presumed to come from the windows of the chapel of God's House, which was refounded as Christ's College by the Lady Margaret Beaufort in 1506. The three smaller figures date from about 1506–10, when the original chapel was modified after the refoundation; they were probably made by Thomas Peghe, who was paid for glass in the chapel on 29 March 1510. All five figures 'exhibit the style of the royal workshop in London carrying on the English tradition', and are among examples of the 'latest Gothic glass-painting' in this country. Edward the Confessor was no doubt included in the series as one of the avowries or patrons of Henry VII; usually depicted as an old man, he is given a youthful appearance in this figure. His emblem of a ring refers to the legend of his giving a ring to St. John in the guise of a pilgrim. Besides these five portraits in the chapel windows, four others are known to have existed in the middle of the eighteenth century, evidently, from their subjects, part of the later and smaller series of figures. They depicted John Beaufort, Duke of Somerset, and his wife Margaret Holland, father and mother of the Lady Margaret Beaufort, and her first and second husbands, Edmund Tudor, Earl of Richmond, and Thomas Stanley, Earl of Derby.[a] Portraits of King Henry 7th. and some other Persons related to the Foundress' are recorded by *Masters* about 1790 as being at whole-length in the east window of the chapel.[b]

REPRODUCED. *Archaeological Journal*, cix (1952), pl. XIIB.

NOTES. (a) This account is taken from Bernard Rackham, 'The ancient windows of Christ's College Chapel, Cambridge', *Archaeological Journal*, cix (1952), 132–51.
(b) Page 28.

ELIZABETH OF YORK

1465–1503. Queen of Henry VII, the marriage uniting the Houses of York and Lancaster. [*D.N.B.*].

25 Artist unknown

Painting on glass, 29 × 17½ in. (73.7 × 44.4 cm.). Whole-length, kneeling in prayer, turned, facing and looking three-quarters left. Wears a coronet; flowing blue dress. To left a book lies open on a red-covered prayer-desk. To left in the background a slanting window, and behind the figure a green hanging edged with red falls from a red canopy.

See no. **24**. Companion figure to that of Henry VII, no. **43**.

REPRODUCED. *Archaeological Journal*, cix (1952), pl. XIIB.

FINCH, SIR JOHN

1626–1682. Admitted 1645, but removed to Balliol College, Oxford; B.A. 1649. Famous for his friendship with Sir Thomas Baines (*q.v.*). Finch became ambassador at Constantinople, taking Baines as his personal physician. He too had studied medicine, becoming Professor at Pisa, where the Grand Duke of Tuscany 'furnished him with all things convenient for the making of experiments in the way of physick'. [*D.N.B.; Peile,* i, 492; *Venn*, I.ii, 138].

26   By SIR PETER LELY

$24\frac{5}{8} \times 21\frac{1}{4}$ in. (62.5 × 53.9 cm.). Canvas. Bust, turned nearly profile left, facing half left, looking front. Bare-headed, long curling brown hair; clean-shaven. Wears black dress, with white falling collar tied with tasselled strings. Within a painted oval. Inscribed lower left, 'Sir John Finch'.

Given by George F. Roe, 1947.[a] Coll. Finch family, Burley-on-the-Hill, Leicestershire (formerly Rutland); descended to Major James Hanbury; his sale, Christie's, 20 June 1947 (61).

See under Sir Thomas Baines, no. **2**.

REPRODUCED. A. Malloch, *Finch and Baines* (1917), p. 31.

NOTE. (a) College Meeting, 4 October 1947, minute 12. The gift was made to commemorate the centenary of the tenancy of a College property by Mr. Roe's family firm.

27   By JOSEPH CATTERNS

$24 \times 19\frac{1}{2}$ in. (60.9 × 49.5 cm.), oval. Marble relief. Bust, turned facing and looking quarter right. Bare-headed, hair curling to the shoulders; clean-shaven. Bust draped.

Given by Daniel, second Earl of Nottingham, *c.* 1684.

See under Sir Thomas Baines, no. **3**.

FISHER, JOHN

1459–1535. Student at Michaelhouse; Master of Michaelhouse from 1497; Vice-Chancellor 1501; first Lady Margaret Professor of Divinity 1503; Confessor & Chaplain to the Lady Margaret Beaufort (*q.v.*); Chancellor of the University and Bishop of Rochester 1504; President of Queens' 1505–8, bringing Erasmus to Cambridge; assisted Lady Margaret in foundation of Christ's and (after her death) St. John's. Fined for denying validity of Catharine of Aragon's marriage, 1534; deprived and beheaded for refusing Act of Supremacy. [*D.N.B.; Venn*, I.ii, 143; A. B. Emden, *A Biographical Register of the University of Cambridge to 1500* (1963), pp. 229–30; *N.C.B.E.L.*, i, 1923–6].

28   After HANS HOLBEIN

$12 \times 10\frac{1}{4}$ in. (30.5 × 26.0 cm.). Wood. Bust, turned, facing and looking quarter left. Wears soft black cap covering the ears; clean-shaven. Wears episcopal rochet and chimere, with dark brown scarf.

Bought 1884. With the Rev. F. O. White, London, from whom it was bought;[a] exh. C.A.S., 1884 (45).

Derived from the Holbein drawing at Windsor Castle, usually assumed to be of about 1528.[b] A shop-work of mechanical quality, predominantly linear in treatment; of identical character and almost the same dimensions is a portrait of Bishop Stephen Gardiner in the Bodleian Library, Oxford.[c] Both are probably of approximately mid-sixteenth century date.

REPRODUCED. *Christ's College Magazine*, xlii (1935-6), 1.

NOTES. (a) Charles Sayle, 'The portraits of Bishop Fisher', *The Eagle*, xvi (1890-1), 330, but no verification has come to light in the records of Christ's College. (b) K. T. Parker, *The drawings of Hans Holbein . . . at Windsor Castle* (1945), p. 39, no. 13 (rep). (c) Mrs. R. L. Poole, *Catalogue of portraits in . . . Oxford*, i (1912), 14, no. 33.

29 Painter unknown

$26\frac{3}{4} \times 18\frac{5}{8}$ in. (67.9 × 47.2 cm.). Canvas. Half-length standing, turned, facing and looking quarter left. Wears black cap covering the ears; clean-shaven. Wears episcopal rochet and chimere with black scarf. Hands held together in prayer. Before him and to the left lies a miniature skeleton; at the left side is a crucifix; and above his head is the inscription, 'IOHANNES : ROFFĒSIS'.

Given by Sir Bruce Ingram, O.B.E., 1956.

Seventeenth or possibly eighteenth-century copy of a painting on wood, of about the middle of the sixteenth century, at St. John's College, Cambridge,[a] in which the crucifix and skeleton appear to be additions probably of the seventeenth century. An example of this portrait-type of Fisher, without the additions, is at Trinity College, Cambridge. The crucifix and particularly the skeleton are typical emblems of the preoccupation of Counter-Reformation thought with ideas of death. The figure itself recalls the portrait of Bishop Foxe by Joannes Corvus at Corpus Christi College, Oxford, though the portrait-type of Fisher to which it belongs is ultimately derived from the Holbein drawing of him at Windsor Castle (see no. **28** above).

NOTE. (a) Rep. *Connoisseur*, cxxxix (1957), 214.

FITZPATRICK, THOMAS CECIL

1861-1931. Admitted 1881; B.A. 1885, Hon. D.D. 1920. Fellow 1888-93, Supernumerary Fellow 1893-1906, Chaplain 1888-1906, Dean 1890-1906. President of Queens' College, 1906-31; University Assistant Demonstrator in Experimental Physics 1888-1906. [*Peile*, ii, 681; *Venn*, II.ii, 513].

30 By J. SEYMOUR LUCAS, R.A., 1907

$12 \times 9\frac{7}{8}$ in. (30.5 × 25.1 cm.). Red chalk. Head and shoulders, turned, facing and looking half left. Bare-headed, receding hair; moustache. With suit wears a turned-down collar with a flat bow tie. Signed and dated below, 'Seymour Lucas/1907'.

(?) Bequeathed by Dr. T. C. Fitzpatrick, 1931. Commissioned by the Subscribers, who gave it to Dr. Fitzpatrick, 1907; exh. R.A., 1907 (1395).

REPRODUCED. *Royal Academy pictures* (1907), p. 99.

31 By J. SEYMOUR LUCAS, R.A.

$13\frac{1}{4} \times 11$ in. (33.7 × 28.9 cm.). Black, red and white chalk. Description as for no. **30** above. Signed and dated lower right, 'Seymour Lucas/May 30th 1907'. Given by the Subscribers, 1907.

Members of Christ's College in residence when Dr. Fitzpatrick became President of Queens' College in 1906, subscribed in 1907 to have two portraits drawn of him. One, which was exhibited at the Royal Academy, was presented to Dr. Fitzpatrick in June 1907, and the other was given to the College by the subscribers.[a]

NOTE. (a) *Christ's College Magazine*, xxi (1906-7), 128 and xxii (1907-8), 31.

FRASER, PETER LOVETT

*c.*1773-1852. Admitted 1790, B.A. 1795. Fellow 1802; Rector of Kegworth (Leics.) & Prebendary of Lincoln 1831. A powerful writer, famous for his leaders in *The Times* written 'in Walter's parlour'. Left valuable collection of books to College library. [*Peile*, ii, 329; *Venn*, II.ii, 570].

32   By JOHN TERNOUTH, 1828

Bust, $27\frac{7}{8}$ in. high (including base $5\frac{1}{4}$ in. high; 70.8 cm., base 13.3 cm.). White marble. Turned front, facing and looking slightly right. Bare-headed, curly hair; clean-shaven but for slight side-whiskers. A folded drapery passes round the neck over a loose robe, leaving the throat bare. Signed and dated at the back, 'TERNOUTH, Sc./1828'.

Bequeathed by the sitter, 1852.[a] Exh. R.A., 1828 (1147).

NOTE. (a) Agreement Book 1842-60, meeting 26 November 1852.

GOODMAN, GEORGE

1821-1908. Admitted 1840, B.A. 1844. Priest 1846; Canon of Melbourne, Australia, 1879-1905. [*Peile*, ii, 469; *Venn*, II.iii, 84].

33   By CANON G. F. WESTON

$5\frac{1}{4}$ × 4 in. (13.3 × 10.1 cm.). Pencil. To knees, seated in a carved armchair, turned, facing and looking nearly profile left, arms resting on the arms of the chair. Bare-headed; clean-shaven but for side-whiskers. Wears jacket, waistcoat and trousers, with high collar and stock.

Given by Mrs. C. W. Benson, daughter of Canon Weston, 1923.[a]

Probably drawn by Canon Weston while an undergraduate at Christ's College, 1840-44. See also nos. **5, 34, 40, 48, 51, 69, 79, 93, 94, 96, 100**.

NOTE. (a) College Meeting, 15 March 1923, minute 12.

GRAHAM, JOHN

1794-1865. Admitted 1811, B.A. 1816, D.D. 1831. Fellow 1816; Tutor 1828-30; Prebendary of Lincoln 1828. Master of Christ's 1830-48, in which capacity he made an abortive attempt to radically reform the college statutes. Vice-Chancellor 1831 and 1840. Bishop of Chester 1848-65. Chaplain to Prince Consort. [*D.N.B.; Peile*, ii, 369; *Venn*, II.iii, 108].

34   By CANON G. F. WESTON

$5\frac{1}{4}$ × 4 in. (13.3 × 10.1 cm.). Pencil. Head and shoulders, turned slightly right, facing and looking half right. Bare-headed; clean-shaven. Wears jacket and waistcoat, with high collar and stock.

Given by Mrs. C. W. Benson, daughter of Canon Weston, 1923.[a]

Probably drawn by Canon Weston while an undergraduate at Christ's College, 1840–44. See also nos. **5, 33, 40, 48, 51, 69, 79, 93, 94, 96, 100.**

NOTE. (a) College Meeting, 15 March 1923, minute 12.

GRIFFITH, ARTHUR FOSTER

1856–1933. Admitted 1875, B.A. 1879. Related to Foster family of Cambridge, millers & bankers. Solicitor & barrister; notable as amateur geologist and antiquary; bequeathed collection of maps, pictures & antiquarian material to the College. [*Peile*, ii, 640; *Venn*, II.iii, 150].

35   Cameograph, 1924

Relief plaque, $8\frac{7}{8}$ × 7 in. (22.6 × 17.8 cm.). Bronze. Bust, profile right. Bare-headed, bald; clean-shaven. Wears jacket and waistcoat. Inscribed right, 'ARTHUR GRIFFITH/1924'.

Source of acquisition unknown.[a]

Another example is in the Department of Geology (Sedgwick Museum), stamped lower left, 'Cameograph/copyright'.[b]

NOTES. (a) Perhaps given by the sitter, as he was the donor in 1924/25 of the example in the Department of Geology, see *Goodison*, p. 150. (b) *Ibid*.

GROSE, SYDNEY WILLIAM

1886–1980. Admitted 1905, B.A. 1908; University Student, British School at Athens, 1909–10. Fellow 1917, Senior Tutor, Praelector, Librarian & Wine-steward. Specialist in Greek numismatics; Hon. Keeper of Coins, Fitzwilliam Museum. [*Peile*, ii, 882].

36   By EDMOND XAVIER KAPP, 1966   PLATE XII

$15\frac{5}{8}$ × $12\frac{7}{8}$ in. (39.7 × 32.8 cm.). Black chalk on white paper. Head and shoulders, turned and facing half left. Bare-headed, clean-shaven. Wears jacket and waistcoat, knotted tie. Signed and dated lower right, 'Kapp '66'.

Commissioned by Christ's College, 1966.

A very good likeness.

GUNNING, HENRY

1768–1854. Admitted 1784, B.A. 1788. Esquire Bedell of the University 1789–1854 (senior from 1827). Author of *Reminiscences*, a valuable if not wholly accurate account of university and college life. [*D.N.B.; Peile*, ii, 318; *Venn*, II.iii, 172].

37 By J. T. WOODHOUSE, M.D.

$29\frac{1}{2} \times 24\frac{1}{2}$ in. (74.9 × 62.2 cm.). Canvas. Half-length seated, turned half left, facing slightly left, looking front, the left hand just visible lower left holding a paper. Bare-headed, bald, dark hair; dark side-whiskers. Wears black jacket with high collar, round his neck a broad blue riband on which hangs a gold medal.

Source of acquisition unknown. Coll. C. H. Cooper, Cambridge, in 1854;[a] his widow in 1890;[b] in the College by 1897.[c]

The gold medal he wears was presented to Gunning, who was an ardent Whig, by a body of Cambridge electors in recognition of his activities in support of the Reform Bill of 1832.[d] As he is wearing the medal, the portrait may have been painted to commemorate this event (or both of them); the blue of the riband may have been the local Whig colour. It cannot be later than 1845, the date of the death of Woodhouse, who was a local doctor and amateur painter.

NOTES. (a) *Gentleman's Magazine*, n.s., xli (1854), (i), 207. (b) *D.N.B.*; the biography is by Thompson Cooper, son of C. H. Cooper. (c) Listed by *Atkinson and Clark*, p. 414. (d) *Loc. cit.*, note (a).

HADDON, ALFRED CORT

1856–1940. Admitted 1875, B.A. 1879, Sc.D. 1897. Fellow 1901, Reader in Ethnology 1909. Anthropologist celebrated for reports of expeditions to the Torres Straits. F.R.S. 1899. [*D.N.B. 1931–40; Peile*, ii, 644; *Venn*, II.iii, 184].

38 By P. A. de LASZLO, 1925

$29\frac{3}{8} \times 24\frac{1}{2}$ in. (74.6 × 62.2 cm.). Half-length, turned half right, facing slightly right, looking front. Bare-headed, white hair; grey moustache; wears gold-rimmed spectacles. Over dark jacket and waistcoat, wears scarlet Sc.D. gown and hood. Dated and signed lower right, '1925. de László'.

Given by friends and pupils of the sitter, 1925.

'Painted last Spring on a commission from a circle of Dr. Haddon's friends and pupils, who wished to celebrate his 70th. birthday and to commemorate his services to anthropology by presenting his portrait to the College. Mr. László generously painted two more portraits of Dr. Haddon, one of which he gave to Dr. Haddon's family and the other to the Anthropological Museum; these are not replicas, but different pictures. All three portraits are admirable.'[a]

NOTE. (a) *Christ's College Magazine*, xxxiv (1924–6), 185; see also *Goodison*, p. 55.

HAMILTON, CLAUDE KENNETH

1901–1978. Admitted 1919, B.A. 1922. Adjutant in the Cambridge University Officers' Training Corps and afterwards a Lieutenant-Colonel.

39 By R. TAIT McKENZIE

Head 11 in. high (including base $3\frac{1}{4}$ in. high; 27.9 cm., base 8.2 cm.). Bronzed plaster. Turned front, facing and looking half left. Bare-headed, clean-shaven. Source of acquisition unknown.[a]

When young. Perhaps connected with the execution of the figure on the Cambridge War Memorial (Station Road) by Tait McKenzie, 1922, for which he was the model.

NOTE. (a) Perhaps bequeathed in 1927 by Sir Arthur E. Shipley, Master of Christ's College 1910–27.

HARRISSON, ROBERT EVERSON

1818–1902. Admitted 1837, B.A. 1841. Successively curate of Allington & Sedgbrook (Lincs.) and Fawley (Hants.), then rector of Hannington (Berks.), Bishopstoke and Droxford (both Hants.). [*Peile*, ii, 458; *Venn*, II.iii, 268].

40 By CANON G. F. WESTON
$5\frac{1}{4} \times 4$ in. (13.3 × 10.1 cm.). Pencil. Half-length seated, turned, facing and looking profile right, his hands clasped before him. Bare-headed, dark hair; clean-shaven. Wears jacket with high collar and stock.

Given by Mrs. C. W. Benson, daughter of Canon Weston, 1923.[a]

Probably drawn by Canon Weston while an undergraduate at Christ's College, 1840–44. See nos. **5, 33, 34, 48, 51, 69, 79, 93, 94, 96, 100**.

NOTE. (a) College Meeting, 15 March 1923, minute 12.

HENRY VI

1421–1471. King of England 1422–61, 1470–1. Accepted title of founder of God's House (the institution which in 1505 was to be transformed into Christ's College) when in 1448 it was moved from the site destined for King's College, Henry's personal foundation, to the present site of Christ's. [*D.N.B.*; R. A. Griffiths, *The Reign of Henry VI* (1981)].

41 Artist unknown
Painting on glass, $33 \times 19\frac{1}{2}$ in. (83.8 × 49.5 cm.). Half-length standing, turned, facing and looking front, the head inclined to his left. Crowned, long hair; clean-shaven. Wears red mantle with an ermine cape over blue robe, a sceptre in his right hand, the orb in his left. Behind the head is a view of a windowed interior with columns, behind the body is a dark hanging. See no. **24**.

REPRODUCED. A. H. Lloyd, *The early history of Christ's College, Cambridge* (1934), frontispiece; *Archaeological Journal*, cix (1952), pl. XIA.

42 Artist unknown
Painting on glass, 26 × 21 in. (66.0 × 53.3 cm.). Whole-length, kneeling in prayer, turned, facing and looking almost profile right. Crowned, long hair; clean-shaven. Wears brown brocaded mantle with an ermine cape over a red robe. Before him a book lies open on a green-covered prayer desk. At either

side in the background is a slanting window, and behind the figure a red hanging edged with green falls from a green canopy. See no. **24**.

REPRODUCED. *Archaeological Journal*, cix (1952), pl. XIIA.

HENRY VII

1457–1509. King of England 1485–1509. Son of the Lady Margaret Beaufort, foundress of Christ's College. [*D.N.B.;* S. B. Chrimes, *Henry VII* (1972)].

43 Artist unknown

Painting on glass, 29 × 17½ in. (73.7 × 44.4 cm.). Whole-length, kneeling in prayer, turned, facing and looking half right. Crowned, long hair; clean-shaven. Wears gilt armour over mail. To right a book lies open on a prayer-desk. To left in the background is a slanting window, and behind the figure a blue hanging edged with green falls from a red canopy.

See no. **24**. Companion figure to that of Elizabeth of York, no. **25**.

REPRODUCED. *Archaeological Journal*, cix (1952), pl. XIIB.

HOBSON, ERNEST WILLIAM

1856–1933. Admitted 1874, B.A. 1878, Sc.D. 1892. Fellow 1878; Sadlerian Professor of Pure Mathematics 1910–31. F.R.S. 1893. [*Peile*, ii, 634; *Venn*, II.iii, 392].

44 By KENNETH GREEN, 1925

25⅛ × 21½ in. (63.8 × 54.6 cm.). Canvas. Nearly half-length, turned, facing and looking quarter left. Bare-headed, dark grey hair; light moustache, pronounced dark eyebrows. Wears black academical doctor's gown (Sc.D.) over dark grey suit with wing collar and dark tie in a ring. Signed and dated lower right, 'Kenneth Green 1925'.

Given by friends and pupils, 1925.

Commissioned and subscribed for by the donors.

HOPKINS, JOHN

*c.*1757–1831. Admitted 1774, B.A. 1779. Fellow 1785–1806; Praelector, Junior Dean, Tutor, Steward from 1792; held sinecure 'Bourn Pension' from 1805. [*Peile*, ii, 301; *Venn*, II.iii, 438].

45 By SILVESTER HARDING

4⅛ × 3¼ in. (10.4 × 8.2 cm.), oval. Water-colour. Bare-headed, close white wig or powdered hair; clean-shaven. Over black dress with jabot wears black academical gown.

Source of acquisition unknown.[a] Coll. Sir Busick Harwood, M.D., F.R.S. (1745(?)–1814).[b]

A repetition is in the Fitzwilliam Museum (no. 622[c]); for a copy see below no. **46**.

NOTES. (a) Possibly given by J. W. Clark, who gave seven similar portraits by Harding from Sir Busick Harwood's collection to the Fitzwilliam Museum in 1903 (see *Goodison*, p. 85, no. 118). Presumably already in the College by 1913, since it is mounted and framed together with nos. 4 and 21, though it is not mentioned by Peile as the others are. (b) Professor of Anatomy and Downing Professor of Medicine, Cambridge. He had a large number of portraits of contemporary members of the University executed for him in this form by Harding. See F. R. Owst, '*Iconomania* in eighteenth-century Cambridge', in *Proceedings of the Cambridge Antiquarian Society*, xlii (1949), 68–72.

46   After SILVESTER HARDING

$4\frac{5}{16} \times 3\frac{1}{2}$ in. (11.1 × 9.0 cm.), oval. Water-colour. Half-length, turned and facing half right, looking front. Bare-headed, white wig; clean-shaven. Over black dress with jabot wears black academical gown.

Given by Miss Elinor Pugh, 1952.[a]

A mediocre, perhaps amateur, copy after an original by Silvester Harding, two of which are known, see no. **45** above. Hopkins was a family connection of the donor, Miss Pugh, having married Elinor Staple-Steare, step-daughter of the Rev. James Bulwyn Pugh of Sible Hedingham, Essex, her great-great-grandfather.

NOTE. (a) Said to have come from the collection of Sir Busick Harwood, like nos. 4 and 21 above, but it seems unlikely as he employed Harding to make the originals (see note (b) to no. 4 above).

HOWE, JOHN, *Called*

1630–1705. Admitted 1647, but stayed at Christ's for only one year, moving to Brasenose, Oxford, where B.A. 1649. Chaplain and Fellow at Magdalen, Oxford, 1652–55. Chaplain to Oliver Cromwell and his son; later Lecturer at St. Margaret's, Westminster, and Chaplain in Ireland and Holland. An incessant preacher and a leader of non-conformity. [*D.N.B.; Peile*, i, 513; *Venn*, I.ii, 417; *N.C.B.E.L.*, ii, 1610].

47   By JOHN CLOSTERMAN, 1702

$29\frac{1}{2} \times 24\frac{3}{8}$ in. (74.9 × 61.9 cm.). Canvas. Half-length, turned and facing slightly left, looking front. Bare-headed, grey periwig; clean-shaven. Wears red academical gown over black clothes, with wide bands. Within a painted oval. Inscribed in lower left spandrel, 'A.⁰ Dom̄. 1702'; in lower right, 'Æta suae. 80'.

Given by Sir Arthur E. Shipley, Master of Christ's College, 1912.[a] Anon. sale (= Col. E. A. Bulwer), Christie's, 25 November 1911 (37), bt. Leggatt.

Given as a portrait of Howe, but it is improbable for several reasons that this identification is correct. In the first place, the inscription, which appears to be old and is undamaged, is inconsistent with his date of birth, since in 1702 he was seventy-two years of age, not eighty. Secondly, his highest degree was that of Master of Arts, and he appears to be wearing a doctor's scarlet gown. Thirdly, the resemblance to his authentic portraits is not convincing. An engraving by Robert White, which was prefixed to Howe's *Living temple* of 1702 (during his lifetime), and a painting by Kneller in the National Portrait Gallery (no. 265), present a consistent likeness despite differences of portrayal; but though with certain similarities of feature the present portrait does not share this characteristic likeness. An old manuscript label at the back attributes the portrait to Closterman, and it is accepted as 'A modest and somewhat damaged late work'; Closterman died in 1711.[b]

NOTES. (a) College Meeting, 1 March 1912, minute 8. (b) Malcolm Rogers, 'John and John Baptist Closterman', *Walpole Society*, xlix (1983), 267, no. 116.

JONES, JOHN HERBERT

c.1822–1908. Admitted 1840, Scholar 1841; then transferred to Jesus, where B.A. and Fellow 1844. Liverpool clergyman from 1845, becoming Hon. Canon of cathedral there from 1880. [*Peile*, ii, 468; *Venn*, II.iii, 603].

48 By CANON G. F. WESTON

$5\frac{1}{4}$ × 4 in. (13.3 × 10.1 cm.). Pencil and grey wash. Bust, turned, facing and looking half left. Bare-headed; clean-shaven. Wears jacket and waistcoat with high collar and stock.

Given by Mrs. C. W. Benson, daughter of Canon Weston, 1923.[a]

Probably drawn by Canon Weston while an undergraduate at Christ's College, 1840–44. See also nos. **5, 33, 34, 40, 51, 69, 79, 93, 94, 96, 100**.

NOTE. (a) College Meeting, 15 March 1923, minute 12.

KAYE, JOHN

1783–1853. Admitted 1800, B.A. 1804, D.D. 1815. Fellow 1804, Tutor 1808–14, Master 1814–30; Regius Professor of Divinity 1816–27, reviving patristic studies. F.R.S. 1848. Bishop of Bristol 1820–27, then of Lincoln 1828–53, residing for a time at Buckden (Hunts.). [*D.N.B.; Peile*, ii, 347; *Venn*, II.iv, 3].

49 By R. ROTHWELL, about 1832

$55\frac{3}{8}$ × $43\frac{1}{4}$ in. (140.6 × 109.8 cm.). Canvas. Three-quarter length seated, turned half right; facing slightly right, looking front, right hand grasps chair-arm, left elbow on arm of chair, the hand in the air. Bare-headed, close grey wig; clean-shaven. Wears episcopal rochet and chimere with black scarf and bands. Deep red curtain behind the figure; to right a glimpse of the interior of a cathedral.

Given by R. G. C. C. Gregg, about 1907.[a] Exh. R.A., 1832 (5).

NOTE. (a) College Meeting, 18 January 1907, minute 7.

LYNFORD (or LINFORD), THOMAS

1650–1724. Born Cambridge, admitted 1666, B.A. 1670/1. Fellow 1675–86. Rector of St. Edmund, Lombard Street, 1685–1724. Campaigned against Popery, being called by enemies 'the ingenious praevaricator of Cambridge'.

Chaplain to William III & Mary, Canon of Westminster 1723. Benefactor to College buildings and to local charity schools. [*D.N.B.; Peile*, ii, 7; *Venn*, I.iii, 87].

50 (?) By THOMAS MURRAY

$29\frac{5}{8} \times 24\frac{3}{8}$ in. (75.2 × 61.9 cm.). Canvas. Half-length, turned and facing half left, looking front. Bare-headed, light periwig; clean-shaven, rubicund complexion. Wears black academical gown with black scarf and bands. Within a painted oval.

Bequeathed by 'Mr. Lardner' of Cambridge, received 1746.

A letter from Anna Maria Jenon, evidently addressed to the Master of the College, and dated 8 February 1745/6, runs as follows. 'Mr. Lardner, who Some years past, had the pleasure of being known to you, Desired in His Will, that after my Death, a picture of Dr. Lynford's (which you may have seen at Mr. Lardners,) should be sent to the Master of Christ's Colledge to be Hang'd up in His Lodge — I have Chose to send it to you while I live, and I hope it will not be Unacceptable to you, and that you will favour it with a place in your Lodge.' A postscript adds that the portrait is on its way.[a]

William Cole states that Lardner was 'formerly an apothecary in the Petty Cury in Cambridge'.[b]

NOTES. (a) College Muniment Room, Misc. (1) Aq. p. 105. (b) British Library, Add. MS.5821 (Cole's 'Various collections for Cambridgeshire', vol. XX), fol. 77.

MALE, CHRISTOPHER PARR

1820–1903. Admitted 1839, B.A. 1843. Master at King Edward School, Birmingham, 1846–63; Vicar of Cotes Heath (Staffs.) 1863–87. [*Peile*, ii, 466; *Venn*, II.iv, 299].

51 By CANON G. F. WESTON

$5\frac{1}{4} \times 4$ in. (13.3 × 10.1 cm.). Pencil. To knees, seated, turned, facing and looking nearly profile left, hands clasped on his knees. Bare-headed; clean-shaven. Wears jacket and waistcoat with high collar and stock.

Given by Mrs. C. W. Benson, daughter of Canon Weston, 1923.[a]

Probably drawn by Canon Weston while an undergraduate at Christ's College, 1840–44. See also nos. **5, 33, 34, 40, 48, 69, 79, 93, 94, 96, 100.**

NOTE. (a) College Meeting, 15 March 1923, minute 12.

MILDMAY, SIR WALTER

*c.*1522–1589. Admitted Fellow-Commoner *c.*1537–8, but no degree from Christ's. Beginning in Court of Augmentations, where his father had made a fortune, he served Edward VI, Mary and Elizabeth in a succession of largely financial capacities, eventually as Chancellor of the Exchequer 1566–89. Knighted 1547. Founder of Emmanuel College 1584; gave books to Christ's library and appointed Laurence Chaderton, of Christ's, first Master of Emmanuel. [*D.N.B.; Peile*, i, 24; *Venn*, I.iii, 188].

52   After (?) PAUL VAN SOMER

$29\frac{3}{4} \times 24\frac{3}{4}$ in. (75.5 × 60.3 cm.). Canvas. Half-length, turned and facing quarter left, looking front. Wears soft black cap over light brown hair; white moustache and chin beard. Wears black gown with white lace-edged ruff. Inscribed round the frame, '*Effigies honoratissimi viri Gvalteri Mildmaii collegii huius socio commensalis et benefactoris equitis aurati cancellarii fisci reginae Elizabethae a consiliis Collegii Emmanuelis fundatoris.*'[a]

Given by Sir Arthur E. Shipley, Master of Christ's College, 1904.[b]

Copied, with the background details omitted, from the whole-length at Emmanuel College, 1903-4.[c] The original is dated 1588 and was painted for the College.

NOTES. (a) 'Portrait of the most honorable Walter Mildmay fellow commoner and benefactor of this college, knight, Chancellor of the Exchequer to Queen Elizabeth, Privy Counsellor, founder of Emmanuel College.' (b) College Meeting, 20 February 1904, minute 1. (c) Permission for the copy to be made was given by Emmanuel College at a College Meeting on 21 November 1903.

MILTON, JOHN

1608–1674. Admitted 1624/5, B.A. 1628/9. Resided in Cambridge until 1632, probably refusing a Fellowship. Early poems on Cambridge subjects: on the carrier Hobson, on the Vice-Chancellor and Esquire Bedell and notably on Edward King, subject of *Lycidas*. [*D.N.B.*; *Peile*, i, 363; *Venn*, I.iii, 193; *N.C.B.E.L.*, i, 1237–96].

The present collection of Milton portraits owes much to Sir Arthur E. Shipley, Master 1910–27. Besides those listed here, two others are known to have been in the possession of the college but cannot now be traced. These are Montford's original model for the statue in the churchyard of St. Giles, Cripplegate (see *Christ's College Magazine*, xxiv (1909–10), 82) and a miniature of him when young which was at one time in the Lodge (but possibly the Master's private property).

53   By ELEANOR WINSLOW, after (?) CORNELIUS JOHNSON

$19\frac{1}{2} \times 15\frac{5}{8}$ in. (49.4 × 39.7 cm.). Canvas. Half-length, turned and facing slightly left, looking front. Bare-headed, reddish hair. Wears brown and black striped doublet, with flat, wired-out collar edged with lace. Within a painted oval.

Given by J. Pierpont Morgan, 1922.[a]

As a boy. Copy of an original in the Pierpont Morgan Library, New York, U.S.A., inscribed to left of head, 'AETATIS/SVAE 10', to right of head, 'AN. 1618', and lower right, 'JOHN MILTON'. This original is first mentioned in 1681,[b] and was in the possession of Milton's widow at her death in 1737.[c] It has been described as painted by Cornelius Johnson, but the correctness of this is doubtful and the picture is now catalogued by the Morgan Library as 'attributed to Cornelius Johnson'.[d]

NOTES. (a) *Christ's College Magazine,* xxxiii (1921–2), 123. (b) By John Aubrey, see Andrew Clark's edition of his *Brief Lives* (1898), ii, 63. (c) See George Vertue, *Walpole Society*, xviii (1930), 79, and J. F. Marsh, *Transactions of the historic society of Lancashire and Cheshire*, vii (1885), 27*–31*. (d) Stylistically there seems little reason for an attribution to Johnson, which is not known to go back beyond G. B. Cipriani's etching of 1760, when the portrait was in Thomas Hollis's possession.

54   By EDWARD PIERCE[a]   PLATE V

Head and shoulders, $11\frac{5}{8}$ in. high (29.5 cm.). Clay.[b] Turned front, facing and looking quarter left. Bare-headed, long hair curling to the shoulders; clean-shaven. Wide, falling-band collar.

Bequeathed by the Rev. John Disney, D.D., 1816.[c] Coll. George Vertue by 1740;[d] his sale, London, Ford, 17–19 May 1757, first day (39), bt. Sir Joshua Reynolds, who sold it to Thomas Hollis;[e] bequeathed by him to Thomas Brand, later Brand Hollis, 1774, who bequeathed it to the Rev. John Disney, 1804. Exh. Cambridge, Christ's College, Milton Tercentenary, 1908 (1).

It has been broken, but little is lost save for part of the hair at the back. In 1925, when a mould for casting was taken from it,[f] the surface was treated with preservative; in 1946 it was cleaned and the surface consolidated with a wax preparation. Though doubts have been expressed about Edward Pierce's authorship, the head has, rightly, never been questioned as a work of this period. The identification as Milton has also always been accepted, with good reason,[g] but whether it was or was not modelled from the life is unknown.[h] The question is not unaffected by the fact that the head is less than life-size, but it has been suggested that this is due to shrinkage of the clay.[i] The date when the head was made is equally unknown and any estimate must be based on internal evidence. In the past, dates ranging from *c.* 1651[j] to 1658[k] have been put forward; from what can be seen of the shape of the collar, a date of *c.* 1660 or even a little later seems to be indicated,[l] which is not incompatible with the facial appearance. A portrait seal in profile was engraved after the head by Thomas Simon.[m]

REPRODUCED. *Christ's College Magazine*, 1889–90, p. 101; Milton Tercentenary, *The portraits, prints and writings of John Milton* (1908), p. 29; *Voltaire's essay on Milton*, ed. D. Flower (1954), frontispiece; *Christ's College Magazine*, May 1970, cover and p. 159.

NOTES. (a) From two notes made by George Vertue in 1740 and 1742, when the head was in his ownership, it appears that it was then traditionally considered to be the work of Edward Pierce (*c.* 1630–1695) (*Walpole Society*, xxiv (1936), 181, and xxvi (1938), 9). In 1757, Thomas Hollis wrote that about 1754 Vertue told him 'he believed it was done' by Pierce, but adds 'my own impression is, that it was modelled by Abraham Simon' (*Memoirs of Thomas Hollis* (1780), ii, 513). Simon (1622(?)–1692(?)), a medalist and modeller in wax in whose authenticated work no head on this scale is known. Sir Lionel Cust questioned the ascription to Pierce (letter to *The Times*; see *Christ's College Magazine*, xix (1904–5), 1–7), but Pierce's authorship was accepted by Rachael Poole (Mrs. R. Lane Poole) in her study of his work, 'Edward Pierce the sculptor', *Walpole Society*, xi (1923), 37–8. In default of evidence to the contrary, there seems no reason for rejecting the traditional ascription. (b) It has been described as terracotta (Poole, *loc. cit.*), but it is certainly of clay, probably unbaked. (c) J. Hildyard and J. J. Smith,

'Milton's mulberry-tree and bust in Christ's College', *Cambridge portfolio* (1840), ii, 504–05. (d) *Walpole Society*, xxiv (1936), 181. Vertue already knew the head by 1738, the year of publication of an edition of Milton's prose works, with an engraving by Vertue after a drawing from the head by J. Richardson T. (e) *Memoirs of Thomas Hollis* (1780), ii, 513; the year in which Reynolds sold it to Hollis (at a small profit, 12 guineas against a purchase price of £9. 12*s*. 0*d*.) is not stated, but it was in his possession by 1760 (*ibid.*, etching by G. B. Cipriani). (f) The original type cast is in the National Portrait Gallery (no. 2102); six more casts were made for the subscribers, who were Sir Arthur Shipley, Master of Christ's College, C. F. Bell, Sir Edmund Gosse, the Victoria and Albert Museum, the Scottish National Portrait Gallery, the National Gallery of Victoria, Melbourne, Australia. (g) See David Piper, *Catalogue of seventeenth-century portraits in the National Portrait Gallery* (1963), pp. 236, 237–8. (h) Cust (*loc. cit.*) suggested that it was 'adapted from W. Faithorne's engraved *ad vivum* portrait' (see L. Fagan, *The engraved works of William Faithorne* (1888), p. 48), but this seems more than speculative. A recent interesting proposal is that 'it may be connected with a life-mask' (Piper, *op. cit.*, p. 236). (i) *Christ's College Magazine*, xviii (1903-4), 1. (j) *Memoirs of Thomas Hollis*, ii, 619. (k) Poole, *op. cit.*, p. 37. (l) Piper, *op. cit.*, p. 236. (m) *Memoirs of Thomas Hollis*, ii, 513, 619. Neither the seal nor any impression from it is now known.

55 Cast after EDWARD PIERCE

Head and shoulders, $11\frac{1}{8}$ in. high (28.3 cm.). Bronzed plaster. Cast of the above, no. **54**.

(?) Bequeathed by Sir Arthur Everett Shipley, Master of Christ's College, 1927.[a]

NOTE. (a) See note (f) to no. **54** above.

56 By HORACE MONTFORD, after EDWARD PIERCE

Head and shoulders, $23\frac{1}{8}$ in. high (including base, 8 in. high; 58.7 cm., base 20.3 cm.). White marble. Turned front, facing and looking quarter left. Bare-headed, long hair curling to the shoulders; clean-shaven. Wide falling-band collar over drapery. Inscribed at front along the cut-off, 'MILTON'; inscribed at the back, 'H. MONTFORD Sc From the/CLAY MODEL MADE FROM THE LIFE/By . . . PEIRCE'; dated at the side, '1903'.

Commissioned by private subscription in the College, 1903.[a] Exh. Cambridge, Christ's College, Milton Tercentenary, 1908 (3).

This reproduces the clay head by Edward Pierce, no. **54** above, enlarged to life-size.[b]

NOTES. (a) *Christ's College Magazine*, xviii (1903–4), 1. (b) *Ibid.*, referring to the smaller size of the Pierce head as due to shrinkage of the clay, for which 'it has been possible to allow in the reproduction'.

57 Sculptor unknown, later 18th century

Bust, $20\frac{1}{4}$ in. high (including base $4\frac{1}{2}$ in. high; 51.3 cm., base 11.4 cm.). Plaster, blacked. Turned, facing and looking front, the head held forward. Bare-headed, hair falling in ringlets to the shoulders; clean-shaven. Wears doublet with deep band-collar, fastened with tasselled strings; drapery falls from the left shoulder across the front of the bust.

Source of acquisition unknown. Exh. Cambridge, Christ's College, Milton Tercentenary, 1908 (7).[a]

This appears to be derived from the posthumous bust by Michael Rysbrack on Milton's monument in Westminster Abbey, based on W. Faithorne's engraving of 1670 from his *ad vivum* drawing.[b] Another example of this plaster is at Stourhead, Wiltshire, together with similar busts of Dryden and Pope. They are the work of an unknown sculptor, later than Rysbrack and inferior to him, who specialised in busts for libraries, frequently basing them on a known original.[c]

NOTES. (a) Lent by Christ's College. (b) L. Fagan, *The engraved works of William Faithorne* (1888), p. 48. (c) Thus described by Mrs. M. I. Webb, author of *Michael Rysbrack* (1954).

58 Sculptor unknown, later 19th century
Bust, $24\frac{3}{4}$ in. high (including base $4\frac{1}{8}$ in. high; 62.9 cm., base 10.4 cm.). Plaster. Turned, facing and looking front. Bare-headed, long hair falling in ringlets to the shoulders; clean-shaven. Wears doublet with long band-collar fastened with tasselled strings; drapery carried behind the head from the right shoulder falls from the left across the front of the bust. Incised stamp at the back, 'J. M. Bloomfield/Paddington'.

Source of acquisition unknown. Exh. Cambridge, Christ's College, Milton Tercentenary, 1908 (6).[a]

Apparently derived from the bust by Rysbrack on Milton's monument in Westminster Abbey (see no. 57 above). Probably of the later nineteenth century.

NOTE. (a) Lent by Christ's College, and incorrectly described as of stone.

MILTON, JOHN, *Called*

59 Attributed to SIR PETER LELY
$21\frac{1}{4} \times 17\frac{3}{8}$ in. (53.9 × 44.1 cm.). Canvas. Bust, turned and facing half right, looking front. Bare-headed, long fair hair; clean-shaven. Dark dress with lace-edged white falling collar.

Source of acquisition unknown. Coll. Rev. J. Hildyard (1809–1887);[a] exh. C.A.S., 1885 (124); Cambridge, Christ's College, Milton Tercentenary, 1908 (22), lent by Christ's College.

Included in the Milton Tercentenary Exhibition among 'pretended portraits', though regarded as a possible portrait of him as a boy.[b] The painting, in fact, depicts a young man, who appears to be not more than about twenty-five years old at the most, and, apart from questions of likeness, this rules out an identification as Milton on grounds of age. The date of the portrait is indicated by the collar he is wearing, which is unlikely to be much earlier than 1648,[c] and in this year Milton became forty. Though the question of likeness is irrelevant, it may be noted, apart from other considerations, that the cloven chin is unknown in Milton's portraiture.

REPRODUCED. Milton Tercentenary, *The portraits, prints and writings of John Milton* (1908), p. 34.

NOTES. (a) Milton Tercentenary, *The portraits, prints and writings of John Milton* (1908), pp. 22, 34. Hildyard was a fellow of Christ's College from 1833 to 1847, and is said to have purchased the portrait about the middle of the nineteenth century. (b) *Ibid.* (c) Such a collar is shown in portraits of Charles I at his trial in January 1649, e.g. at All Souls College, Oxford.

60 Painter unknown, *c.*1650

29 × 23 in. (73.6 × 58.4 cm.). Canvas. Half-length, turned and facing slightly right, looking front, a book with clasps held across in the right hand, the first finger between the leaves. Bare-headed, long brown hair; clean-shaven. Wears black academical gown over black dress, with white falling collar tied with tasselled cords; white cuffs edged with black point lace. Inscribed as on a tablet, upper right, 'NEC INGRATVS NEC INVTILIS/VIDEAR VIXISSE'.[a]

Given by James Cartmell, D.D., Master of Christ's College (1810-1881). Coll. Mrs. Clabborn, Cambridge;[b] her sale at no. 5 Trumpington Street, Cambridge, 18 June 1851 (104), bt. Dr. Cartmell; exh. C.A.S., 1885 (125).

From the costume, this is of about the middle of the seventeenth century, and as a very young man is depicted the date alone rules it out as a portrait of Milton, to whose authentic portraits, in any case, it bears no resemblance. An alternative identification as Francis Quarles (1592-1644) has been suggested,[c] but this too is impossible on grounds of date.

NOTES. (a) 'May I be seen to have been neither useless nor unthankful'. (b) From a note at the back of the picture, which says also that it had been bought some years previously at another sale by Mrs. Clabborn's son-in-law, Mr. Cannon, a solicitor. (c) John Peile, *Christ's College* (1900). p. 127 n.

61 Painter unknown, *c.*1655-60

$17\frac{5}{8} \times 15\frac{3}{8}$ in. (44.7 × 39.1 cm.). Canvas. Bust, turned and facing quarter left, looking front. Bare-headed, light brown hair curling to the shoulders; clean-shaven. Wears black dress with wide band-collar.

Given by F. H. Cripps Day, 1950. Coll. J. Seymour Lucas, R.A.; his sale, Christie's, 15 December 1922 (5), bt. Cripps Day.

This was sold at Christie's as of Milton by Mary Beale, and was given as such. It certainly is not by Mary Beale, nor can it be accepted as depicting Milton. From the band-collar he wears, the portrait cannot be earlier than about the middle of the sixteen-fifties, so that it is of approximately the same date as the clay head by Edward Pierce, no. **54** above. From a comparison, a certain general similarity emerges to explain the identification, but in both features and expression there are fundamental differences between the two, particularly noticeable in the shape of the mouth.

OLDFIELD, JOSHUA, *Called*

1656–1729. Admitted at Magdalene 1673/4. Said to have studied at Christ's and at Lincoln College, Oxford, but graduated from none, reputedly from 'dislike to subscription'. Received Presbyterian orders at Mansfield, 1687, and was pastor of congregations at Oxford, and at Coventry and London, where he also had a highly regarded 'academy' for training dissenting ministers. Nevertheless in trouble with authorities for theological views and preaching without licence. Intimate with Locke. [*D.N.B.; Peile*, ii, 40; *Venn*, I.iii, 278].

62 Painter unknown

$22\frac{3}{4} \times 19\frac{1}{4}$ in. (57.8 × 48.8 cm.). Canvas. Half-length, turned profile right, facing half right, looking front. Bare-headed, long, dark brown hair; clean-shaven. Wears golden-brown robe over open-necked white shirt. At right a canvas on an easel with a design sketched on it.

Bought 1912.[a] Coll. Colonel E. A. Bulwer, sold (anon.) Christie's, 25 November 1911 (3), bt. Leggatt; Sir Arthur E. Shipley, Master of Christ's College, from whom it was bought.

Bought as a portrait of Oldfield, but impossible as such on grounds of date alone, since from the costume and style of painting it must be of about 1650–60, and it represents a man of about thirty years of age.[b] The canvas before which he sits (scarcely appropriate for a divine, let alone a dissenting one) suggests that this is a portrait of a painter, perhaps a self-portrait. In a general way it is somewhat reminiscent of the portrait of Oliver de Crats in the Ashmolean Museum, Oxford (cat. 1962, no. 125).

NOTES. (a) College Meeting, 1 March 1912, minute 8. (b) The identification as Oldfield is evidently of long standing, as it appears on a label apparently of the eighteenth century on the stretcher. Perhaps it was based on the painting which was the original of an engraving in Walter Wilson's *The history and antiquities of dissenting churches*, iv (1814), 160, showing a man with similar, though different, features.

OUTRAM (or OWTRAM), WILLIAM

1626–1679. B.A. 1645/6, M.A. 1649, D.D. 1662. Fellow of Trinity College 1647–8, of Christ's College 1648–57; Rector of St. Margaret's, Westminster, 1664–79; Prebendary of Westminster 1670. Author of celebrated *De Sacrificiis*. [*D.N.B.; Peile*, i, 483; *Venn*, I.iii, 291].

63 By MARY BEALE, 1672

$28\frac{1}{2} \times 24\frac{5}{8}$ in. (72.3 × 62.5 cm.). Canvas. Half-length, turned half right, facing nearly half right, looking front. Wears black skull cap over fair hair falling to his shoulders; clean-shaven. Wears black academical gown with black scarf, wide bands. Within a painted sculptural oval.

Bought 1883.[a] With the Rev. F. O. White from whom it was bought;[b] exh. C.A.S., 1885 (137).

Of coarse quality. Presumably the portrait referred to by her husband Charles Beale as having been painted in 1672.[c]

ENGRAVED. Line-engraving by Robert White.[d]

NOTES. (a) Agreement Book, 1860-95, 15 February 1883, minute 7. (b) He was at this time of 43 Arundel Square, Barnsbury, London; as a dealer between 1870 and 1899 he specialised in portraits of dignitaries of the Church of England. (c) The entry in his note-book is printed in *Walpole Society*, xxiv (*Vertue Note Books* vol. iv, 1936), 170. (d) Frontispiece to Outram's *Twenty sermons* (1697).

PALEY, WILLIAM

1743-1805. Admitted 1758, B.A. 1763, D.D. 1795. Fellow 1766, Senior Dean 1775; Prebendary of Carlisle 1780-95, Archdeacon 1782-1805, Chancellor of diocese 1785-1805, Prebendary of St. Paul's 1794, Sub-dean of Lincoln & Vicar of Bishop Wearmouth (Co. Durham) 1795-1805; author of many textbooks, notably *The Evidences of Christianity*, 1794, set as text for Cambridge entrance until 1920. [*D.N.B.*; *Peile*, ii, 267; *Venn*, II.v, 10; *N.C.B.E.L.*, ii, 1890].

64 By SIR WILLIAM BEECHEY, R.A., after GEORGE ROMNEY

$29\frac{5}{8}$ × $24\frac{3}{8}$ in. (75.2 × 61.9 cm.). Canvas. Half-length, turned and facing half right, looking front. Wears three-cornered black hat over white wig; clean-shaven. Black dress.

Copied by Sir William Beechey for Christ's College, 1808-9.[a]

The original by Romney is a three-quarter length portrait, painted for Edward Law, first Baron Ellenborough; sittings 1789, completed 1791. His son, the first Earl of Ellenborough (b.1790), to whom the painting then belonged, stated in 1862 that 'it was, I think, copied for Christ's College when I was a boy'.[b] The Romney is now in the National Portrait Gallery (no. 3659), together with another half-length copy ascribed to Beechey (no. 145). It has been suggested on grounds of style that the College portrait is by Beechey's son, G. D. Beechey (1798-1852),[c] but the date of his birth rules this out.

NOTES. (a) Beechey's account, addressed to the Master of the College, the Rev. Dr. Thomas Browne, and dated 13 January 1809, is in the College archives. The charge for the portrait was £42. 0s. 0d., and sundry expenses include 'Porterage of Picture from Lord Ellenborough and back'. The painting was that day being sent from Beechey's house in Harley Street, London, to Cambridge. In Beechey's Account Books, under 6 January 1809, an entry of the charge of £42 for the portrait reads, 'Of Mr. Brown, for a copy of Dr. Paley' (W. Roberts, *Sir William Beechey, R.A.* (1907), p. 229). (b) H. Ward and W. Roberts, *Romney* (1904), ii, 116. (c) By J. D. Milner, Director of the National Portrait Gallery (*Christ's College Magazine*, xxvi (1911-12), 15). G. D. Beechey first exhibited portraits in 1817.

PEILE, JOHN

1838-1910. Admitted 1856, B.A. 1860, Litt.D. 1884. Fellow 1860-87 (vacated through marriage 1866 but reinstated 1867), Tutor 1861-84; Reader in Comparative Philology 1884-91. Master of the College 1887-1910, Vice-Chancellor 1891-3. Author of books on the College, notably the *Biographical Register*. [*D.N.B. 1901-11; Peile*, ii, 545; *Venn*, II.v, 76].

65   By SIR GEORGE REID, P.R.S.A.

$26\frac{1}{2} \times 21\frac{1}{2}$ in. (67.3 × 54.6 cm.). Canvas. Half-length, turned nearly profile right, leaning somewhat forward, facing half right, looking front. Bare-headed, grey hair; grey beard and moustache; wears spectacles. Over dark brown clothes wears scarlet Litt.D. gown. Signed lower right, 'R'.

Given by the subscribers, 1902.

Subscribed for by 'members of the College and other friends' and painted for the subscribers; a replica was given to Dr. Peile.[a]

NOTE. (a) *Christ's College Magazine*, xvii (1902–3), 20.

PERKINS, WILLIAM

1558–1602. Admitted 1577, B.A. 1580/1. Fellow 1584–95, Dean 1590–91. Reputedly a reformed drunkard whose recourse to extreme puritanism brought him before the Vice-Chancellor in 1587 and 1591. Lecturer at Great St. Andrew's church, where his sermons attracted large numbers from town and university. [*D.N.B.*; *Peile*, i, 141; *Venn*, I.iii, 347; *N.C.B.E.L.*, i, 1931–2].

66   Painter unknown

$10\frac{5}{8} \times 8\frac{1}{2}$ in. (27.0 × 21.5 cm.). Wood. Short half-length, turned and facing slightly left, looking front. Bare-headed, receding reddish fair hair; reddish beard and moustache. Wears black gown over black doublet, with narrow white ruff. Holds before him in both hands an open brown book; the right hand is deformed, with no thumb and only one finger.

Source of acquisition unknown. *Masters* p. 28, no. 10.

Probably of the fairly early seventeenth century, rather crude in quality. Though close to the engraving of Perkins in Henry Holland's *Herωologia Anglica* (1620), p. 219, it shows both hands holding the book, whereas in the engraving he slightly raises the left hand in an expository gesture. The engraving is also suggestive of an original of much better quality than the present portrait.[a] A larger version on wood, of similar date, is at Sidney Sussex College, Cambridge (below, no. **176**).

NOTE. (a) The *Dictionary of National Biography* (1896) states erroneously that the *Herωologia* engraving is after the Christ's College portrait, which is also put forward as a possibility in A. M. Hind, *Engraving in England in the sixteenth and seventeenth centuries*, ii (1955), 158.

PLUMB, SIR JOHN HAROLD

Born 1911. University College Leicester; B.A. (London) 1933, Ph.D. 1936, Litt.D. 1957. Ehrman Research Fellow, King's College 1939–46 (Foreign Office 1940–45). Fellow of Christ's 1946, Steward 1948–50, Tutor 1950–59, Master 1978–82. Professor of Modern English History 1966–74. Historian of the eighteenth century and biographer of Walpole. [*Who's Who*].

67 By SIR LAWRENCE GOWING, C.B.E.

$31\frac{1}{2} \times 39\frac{1}{2}$ in. (80.0 × 100.3 cm.). Canvas. In an interior, at half-length, seated centrally at a light brown desk, covered with books and papers, reading a book turned half left. Bare-headed, spectacles, grey suit. Behind the figure, to right a double door, one leaf open, with a semi-circular fanlight above, to left a lighted electric lamp with a yellow shade; further to left, a picture on a return wall, extreme left a brown cabinet. A reading lamp is on the desk, in front of which is a small table with papers on it. The room has light blue walls.

Commissioned by Christ's College, 1979.

68 By JENNY POLAK

$35\frac{5}{8} \times 33\frac{5}{8}$ in. (90.5 × 85.4 cm.). Whole-length, in an interior, seated in a buff upholstered mahogany armchair, turned half left, the head half right, hands clasped in his lap. Bare-headed, clean-shaven, wears a dark blue suit with a bow tie, spectacles. To left, an open window with pink curtains, to right part of a cabinet containing china, in front of which is a pink-upholstered stool. White wall and window paint, grey floor.

Commissioned by Christ's College, 1980.

PURCHAS, JOHN

1823–1872. Born Cambridge, son of mayor. Admitted 1840, B.A. 1844. Clergyman. As perpetual curate of St. James', Brighton, subjected to a relentless prosecution for ritualistic practices which reached the Privy Council. [*D.N.B.; Peile*, ii, 470; *Venn*, II.v, 219].

69 By CANON G. F. WESTON

$5\frac{1}{4} \times 4$ in. (13.3 × 10.1 cm.). Pencil. To knees seated, turned, facing and looking half right, right arm resting on a table with a quill pen in his hand, left hand resting on his thigh. Bare-headed, long hair covering his ears; clean-shaven. Wears jacket, waistcoat and trousers, with high collar and stock.

Given by Mrs. C. W. Benson, daughter of Canon Weston, 1923.[a]

Probably drawn by Canon Weston while an undergraduate at Christ's College, 1840-44. See also nos. **5, 33, 34, 40, 48, 51, 79, 93, 94, 96, 100**.

NOTE. (a) College Meeting, 15 March 1923, minute 12.

RAVEN, CHARLES EARLE

1885–1964. Admitted Scholar of Caius 1904, B.A. 1907, D.D. 1923. Fellow, Dean & Lecturer, Emmanuel, 1909–20; Canon of Liverpool 1924–32, Chancellor of Liverpool 1931–2, Canon of Ely 1932–40; Fellow of Christ's 1932, Master 1939–50; Regius Professor of Divinity 1932–50; Vice-Chancellor 1947–49. Pacifist and naturalist. [*D.N.B. 1961–70*; J. Venn *et al., Biographical History of Gonville & Caius College*, iv, 51, v, 89, vi, 35, vii, 9].

70   By EDMUND J. NELSON, 1949   PLATE XI

$29\frac{3}{4} \times 24\frac{1}{2}$ in. (75.6 × 62.2 cm.). Canvas. Half-length seated, turned, facing and looking half right. Bare-headed, grey hair; clean shaven. Wears scarlet D.D. gown and black scarf over scarlet cassock, with bands. Background, shelves of books. Signed and dated upper left, 'Edmund J. Nelson, 1949'.

Commissioned by the College, 1949. Exh. London, Foyle's Art Gallery, 1953 (8).

The scarlet cassock is that of a royal chaplain, which Dr. Raven became in 1919; the badge of a royal chaplain is visible on the black scarf at his left side. The portrait was commissioned 'in recognition of his holding the Office of Vice-Chancellor, and that at a time of historical significance for College and University alike'.[a] He was Vice-Chancellor from 1947 to 1949.

NOTE. (a) College Meeting, 26 October 1948, minute 22.

RICHMOND AND DERBY, LADY MARGARET BEAUFORT, Countess of

1443–1509. Mother of Henry VII. Under influence of John Fisher, her confessor, first endowed chairs of divinity at Oxford and Cambridge, then founded Christ's College out of nucleus of God's House in 1505 and St. John's College in 1508. [D.N.B.].

Of the following five painted portraits which are acceptable as authentic likenesses, two can be recognised as relatively modern, and two older portraits can be identified from records as acquired in recent times. The one remaining portrait, the standing whole-length (no. **71**), may or may not be identifiable with either of two portraits received at the beginning of the 17th century. One came as a bequest from Dr. Gabriel Goodman, Dean of Westminster, in 1601, who bequeathed also to Sidney Sussex College a portrait of their foundress, Lady Frances Sidney. The other was given 'thru Mr. Montagu's man' in 1602. (John Peile, *Christ's College* (1910), p. 119, and his *Biographical register*, i, 41). The identification with no. **71** of a portrait given by the Lady Margaret's executors between January 1511 and June 1512 (C. H. Cooper, *Memoir of Margaret, Countess of Richmond and Derby* (1874), p. 196) is ruled out on grounds of the date assignable to this whole-length.

71   Unknown English painter, later sixteenth century   PLATE I

$77 \times 41\frac{1}{4}$ in. (195.6 × 104.7 cm.). Wood. Whole-length standing, turned, facing and looking nearly half left, holding a small book open in both hands. Wears white gable hood and chin barbe, which fall to cover the shoulders, with a black mantle over an ample black gown to the feet.[a] Dark brown background; red floor. Upper left, her arms,[b] ensigned with a coronet. The frame inscribed, 'MARGARETA RICHMONDIAE COMITISSA REGIS HENRICI SEPTIMI MATER. OCTAVI AVIA. D. ELIZABETHAE R. PROAVIA QUAE GRAMATICES DOCTOREM APVD WINBORNE, DIVINI VERBI PRAECONEM PER TOTAM ANGLIAM DVOS

ITEM SACRARVM LITERARVM INTERPRETES; ALTERVM OXONIAE ALTERVM
CANTABRIGIAE CONSTUTVIT; VBI ET COLLEGIA DVO CHRISTO, ET IOANNI
EIVS DISCIPVLO FVNDAVIT. OBIIT M.D.IX.III.KAL.IVLII.SEPVLTA IN ECCLESIA
WESTMONASTERIENSI CVI ET BONA NON PAVCA CONTVLIT.'[c] On the open
page of the book is inscribed, 'EGO SVM RESVRRECTIO ET VITA QVI CREDIT
IN ME ETIAM SI MORTVVS FVERIT VIVET. IOAN·XI.'[d]

For acquisition, see p. 34 above. In the possession of the College by 1714;[e]
Masters, p. 28, no. 6; exh. Tudor Exhibition, 1890 (37); Richard III (National
Portrait Gallery), 1973 (P41).

Originally of very good quality, though now much damaged; the face and
hands are much abraded, the hood and barbe considerably rubbed, and the
black mantle and gown probably entirely renewed, as are the background
and floor. The background may at one time have had a large pattern of port-
cullises and Tudor roses among foliage.[f] The arms seem later than the portrait,
but may be a renewal of a coat originally there.[g] When cleaned in 1884,
alterations to the hands were removed revealing them in their present, original
position.[h] This is by far the best of the known painted portraits of the Lady
Margaret Beaufort, and as a standing whole-length of her is unique. The standard portrait of her seems to have been a half-length with hands, in the same
dress of hood, chin barbe, black mantle and gown, most often quite small in
size, which is preserved in numerous examples. Though they vary considerably in character, and probably also in date,[i] they all conform to the same
portrait-pattern, and it is again this established pattern, enlarged to the size
of life and extended to whole-length, which appears in the present imposing
portrait. To judge from its high quality, this must have been taken from an
exceptional prototype, and appears to be the work of an English painter,
since the flesh is painted in a characteristically English technical tradition.
Tree-ring measurements of the panel by Dr. J. M. Fletcher in 1973 and 1977
indicate 1578 as the earliest date for the painting, but for the 'Likely use of
the panel' Dr. Fletcher suggests a date of 1580-90. A half-length version on
wood belonged in 1913 to Mr. Walter Long, Southampton.

If any portraits of the Lady Margaret were painted during her lifetime
nothing is now known of them, but several were painted for her executors
soon after her death. Their accounts refer to two portraits paid for between
25 June 1509 and 24 January 1510,[j] and to a portrait at Christ's College for
which 'Maynerde payntor' received a part payment of sixty shillings between
24 January 1511 and 19 June 1513.[k] This Maynerde also drew or painted on
canvas the design for the effigy on the Lady Margaret's tomb in Westminster
Abbey, for which he received payments from 1511 to 1514,[l] and must thus
have been well acquainted with her likeness. None of the extant portraits of
the Lady Margaret seems likely to be identifiable with those thus recorded,
the one at Christ's has vanished, but it might well be from the portraits
painted for her executors that the standard portraiture of her took its origin.

REPRODUCED. *Connoisseur*, cxxxix (1957), 214; Roy Strong, *National Portrait Gallery, Tudor and Jacobean portraits* (1969), pl. 34.

ENGRAVED. Mezzotint by J. Faber sen., 1714.[m]

NOTES. (a) This nun-like costume is that of a widow or vowess, of which the barbe (worn over the chin in accordance with her rank), the head-dress and the mantle are the chief distinguishing garments. The Lady Margaret took a vow of chastity or widowhood, thus becoming a vowess, in the lifetime of her last husband, Thomas Stanley, Earl of Derby, whom she married shortly before 1482, and renewed it after his death in 1504 (C. H. Cooper, *Memoir of Margaret, Countess of Richmond and Derby* (1874), pp. 97-9). (b) Tudor, France modern and England quarterly within a bordure azure charged with fleur-de-lys and mullets (for her first husband, Edmund Tudor, Earl of Richmond, father of Henry VII), impaling Beaufort, France modern and England quarterly within a bordure compony argent and azure. (c) 'Margaret Countess of Richmond, mother of King Henry VII, grandmother of King Henry VIII, great-grandmother of the late Queen Elizabeth; who established a doctor of grammar at Winborne, a preacher of Holy Writ throughout England, and also two professors of Divinity, one in Oxford and the other in Cambridge, in which place she also founded two colleges, dedicated to Christ and to his disciple John. She died on 29 June 1509 and was buried in the Abbey Church of Westminster, on which also she conferred not a few benefits.' (d) 'I am the resurrection and the life, he that believeth in me, though he were dead, yet shall he live. John 11' (verse 25). (e) The date of Faber's mezzotint (see 'Engraved'). (f) It is thus in Faber's mezzotint. (g) Not only the coat, but the coronet too, corresponds correctly to the heraldry of the Lady Margaret's tomb in Westminster Abbey; a shield of arms surmounted by a coronet is similarly introduced in the portrait of Margaret Pole, Countess of Salisbury, of about 1535 in the National Portrait Gallery (no. 1541). (h) Faber's mezzotint shows the former position, which, curiously enough, is the one usually found in the numerous class of small half-length portraits of the Lady Margaret. (i) For example, the one belonging to the University was given in 1580 (see *Goodison*, p. 2), so this portrait-pattern in a small size was still current towards the end of the sixteenth century. (j) C. H. Cooper, *Memoir of Margaret, Countess of Richmond and Derby* (1874), p. 185. (k) Cooper, *op. cit.*, p. 198. (l) Cooper, *op. cit.*, pp. 200-1. He was almost certainly Maynard Waywyke (Waynwyk, etc.) who is last heard of as resident in All Hallows parish, London, in 1523. (m) J. Chaloner Smith, *British mezzotinto portraits*, Part I (1878), p. 284, no. 34. At half-length in reverse, dedicated to John Covel, Master of Christ's College, one of a series of eighteen engravings of founders of Cambridge colleges, described as 'from the original paintings in Cambridge'. The present whole-length is the only portrait of the Lady Margaret now in the possession of the College which could have been the original of the engraving, and it seems virtually certain that it is this portrait which was used.

72   Unknown English painter, second quarter of the eighteenth century
$69\frac{1}{2} \times 43\frac{1}{4}$ in. (176.5 × 110.5 cm.). Canvas. Whole-length kneeling, turned, facing and looking three-quarters left; hands held together in prayer. Wears white gable hood and chin barbe, with flowing black robes. Before her to left an open book on a prayer desk with a gold-fringed black covering. In the background, behind the figure a pillared classical doorway at an angle, to right a green hanging with her arms, supporters and badges within an oval wreath,[a] to left a Gothic window. At top right and left is draped a dark green curtain.

Source of acquisition unknown. *Masters* p. 28, no. 8.

Similar to a painting of the later sixteenth century, almost the same in size, at St. John's College, Cambridge, from which it is presumably taken, though varied by the introduction of sundry eighteenth-century modifications. St. John's College possesses another variant of much the same date. The head goes back to the same early portrait-pattern as no. **71** above, and nos. **73** and **74** below. The date may be judged from the massive character of the classical doorway in the background and from the oblique angle at which it is set, both suggesting a period probably not very long after 1725.

NOTE. (a) The coat of arms, which is surmounted by a coronet, has as supporters an eagle left, an antelope right, below it is the Beaufort motto, 'Souvent me souvient'; at the bottom is the Beaufort badge of a portcullis, and at the top the Lancastrian badge of a red rose.

73 Unknown English painter, (?) sixteenth century
13 × 8⅜ in. (33.0 × 21.2 cm.). Wood. Bust, turned, facing and looking half left. Wears white gable hood and chin barbe, falling to the shoulders, over black dress.
Bought 1883.[a]
Almost completely covered with coarse old repaint, which has itself been repaired in a number of places. Perhaps originally of the sixteenth century. Of the standard half-length portrait-pattern (see no. **71**); ruddy flesh-colour.

NOTE. (a) Agreement Book 1860–95, meeting 26 February 1883, minute 4, where it is said to have come 'from the sale at Lee Warley', but this is not an identifiable place-name; the accounts give Wright Harvey as the name of the seller.

74 Unknown English painter, sixteenth century
19⅞ × 14⅛ in. (50.5 × 35.9 cm.). Wood. Half-length, turned, facing and looking half left, holding open before her in both hands a red-bound manuscript book. Wears white gable hood falling to shoulders and white chin barbe, over black mantle. Dark green background. A painted angle ornament decorates each upper corner.
(?) Bequeathed by Sir Arthur E. Shipley, Master of Christ's College, 1927. Anon. sale, Sotheby's, 25 February 1925 (62), bt. Leggatt for Sir Arthur Shipley.
Flesh and whites in good condition, background and black mantle repainted. Of the standard half-length portrait-pattern (see no. **71** above); ruddy flesh-colour.

75 Unknown painter, late eighteenth or nineteenth century
24⅜ × 16¾ in. (61.9 × 42.8 cm.). Canvas. Half-length, turned front, facing quarter left, looking front, holding book open flat before her in both hands. Wears white gable hood, barbe falling to the elbows, over black dress.
Source of acquisition unknown. Exh. C.A.S. 1884 (20).
The hood is misunderstood so as to fall in a lappet at each side, that at her right behind the shoulder, that at her left in front of it. The barbe does not cover the chin as it should. The standard half-length portrait-pattern 'improved' (see no. **71** above).

76   Cast after PIETRO TORRIGIANO

Effigy, 28 × 24 in. (71.1 × 61.0 cm.). Plaster. Half-length, recumbent, the head supported on two cushions, her hands held in prayer. Wears gable hood and chin barbe falling to her shoulders, with a mantle fastened by cords over a gown.

Given by Sir John Armitage Robinson, K.C.V.O., Dean of Westminster, 1905.[a]

Cast of the upper portion of the whole-length effigy on the tomb of the Lady Margaret in Henry VII's chapel, Westminster Abbey. The contract for the tomb with Pietro Torrigiano, a Florentine sculptor, is dated 23 November 1511, the effigy to be made of gilt copper.[b]

NOTES. (a) College Meeting, 22 August 1905, minute 5. (b) See Sir R. F. Scott, 'Contracts for the tomb of the Lady Margaret Beaufort', *Archaeologia*, lxvi (1915), 365–72.

RICHMOND AND DERBY, LADY MARGARET BEAUFORT,
Countess of, *Called*

77   By WILFRED EGAN after an unknown painter

$17\frac{1}{4}$ × $12\frac{1}{8}$ in. (43.8 × 30.8 cm.). Wood. Half-length, turned, facing and looking half left, the head bent forward, the hands held before her in prayer. Wears embroidered buff gable hood over white coif, black barbe, and brown dress with grey fur cuffs. Rings on the first, third and fourth fingers of the left hand. Upper left, her arms in a lozenge[a] enclosed in a circle inscribed 'MARGARETA BEAUFORT COM$\overset{A}{\underline{}}$ RICHMONDIÆ DERBIÆ'. Dark green background patterned with Tudor roses.

Source of acquisition unknown.

When young. Copy of an original in the National Portrait Gallery (no. 1488), bought in 1908, which X-ray examination shows to be painted over a later Holbeinesque portrait of a woman. The deception is probably a relatively modern one; the likeness as a young woman is valueless, as all the known authentic portraits show her when old. Copied in 1909.

NOTE. (a) The arms of Beaufort, see above, no. 71, n. (b).

78   Painter unknown, second half of the seventeenth century

$14\frac{1}{2}$ × $11\frac{1}{2}$ in. (36.8 × 29.2 cm.). Wood. Half-length, turned and facing very slightly left, looking front, a closed book held before her in both hands. Wears black hood edged with white, falling below the shoulders, with white barbe below the chin, and white habit. Upper left, a crozier with red staff and gold top.

Source of acquisition unknown.

Unlike the Lady Margaret Beaufort in feature, wrong in costume for the attire she wore as a vowess, and unconnected with her standard portrait-pattern. Perhaps French in origin, and possibly a portrait of an abbess.

ROBERTS, JOHN ARTHUR JEAFFRESON

1819–1901. Admitted 1840, B.A. 1845. Clergyman. Various curacies, then Rector of Hamilton, Bermuda, 1852–56. Returned to succession of curacies, then Rector of Byrness (Northumberland) 1888–1901. [*Peile*, ii, 470; *Venn*, II.v, 317].

79　By CANON G. F. WESTON

$5\frac{1}{4}$ × 4 in. (13.3 × 10.1 cm.). Pencil. Bust, turned, facing and looking nearly profile left. Bare-headed; clean-shaven but for side-whiskers. Wears jacket and waistcoat, with high collar and stock. Inscribed below, 'Roberts, Christ's Coll.'.

Given by Mrs. C. W. Benson, daughter of Canon Weston, 1923.[a]

Probably drawn by Canon Weston while an undergraduate at Christ's College, 1840–44. See also nos. **5, 33, 34, 40, 48, 51, 69, 93, 94, 96, 100**.

NOTE. (a) College Meeting, 15 March 1923, minute 12.

ROUSE, WILLIAM HENRY DENHAM

1863–1950. Admitted 1882, B.A. 1886, Litt.D. 1901. Fellow 1888–94, Hon. Fellow 1933. Schoolmaster at Bedford, Cheltenham and Rugby. Headmaster of the Perse School, Cambridge, 1901–28, where he introduced direct teaching methods in the classics and modern languages. Bequests to the college included his home, Histon Manor, and books. [*D.N.B. 1941–50; Peile*, ii, 687; *Venn*, II.v, 367].

80　By GEORGE HAVARD THOMAS, 1928

Bust, $19\frac{1}{8}$ in. high (48.5 cm.). Bronze. Turned front, facing and looking slightly right; without shoulders. Bare-headed, bald; moustache, beard and slight whiskers. Wears jacket and waistcoat with knotted tie. Inscribed at base along the front, 'ROUSE'; signed and dated at the back, 'George Thomas / 1928'.

Given by W. H. D. Rouse, Litt.D., 1949.[a]

Given to Dr. Rouse by the family of (the late) James Havard Thomas, father of George Havard Thomas, on the occasion of Dr. Rouse's retirement from the headmastership of the Perse School, Cambridge, in 1928. The gift was made in recognition of his kindness to a younger son, M. J. Havard Thomas, when a boy at the school from 1922 to 1928. The bust was executed expressly for this purpose, and was presented at the same time as another gift subscribed for by the school.[b] A plaster cast was made in 1951 for Dr. Rouse's cousin, Mr P. G. Rouse,[c] who considered the bust quite a good likeness.

NOTES. (a) College Meeting, 18 June 1949, minute 9. (b) Information kindly supplied by Dr. M. J. Havard Thomas. (c) College Meeting, 16 January 1951, minute 18.

SEELEY, SIR JOHN ROBERT

1834–1895. Admitted 1852, B.A. 1857, Litt.D. 1892. Fellow 1858–69; Professor of Latin, University College, London 1863–9, Regius Professor of Modern History, Cambridge, 1869–95; Fellow of Caius 1882–95, Hon. Fellow of Christ's 1883; K.C.M.G. 1894. Many writings, notably *Ecce Homo* 1865, *Expansion of England* 1893, *Growth of British Policy* 1895. [*D.N.B.; Peile*, ii, 525; *Venn*, II.v, 458; *N.C.B.E.L.*, iii, 1495–6].

81   By CLARA EWALD

$32\frac{1}{8}$ × 28 in. (81.6 × 71.1 cm.). Canvas. Half-length, turned and facing slightly left, looking front, holding up a book before him in his left hand. Bareheaded, grey hair; clean-shaven. Wears scarlet Litt.D. gown over black clothes. Signed lower right, 'Clara Ewald'.

Bought 1900.[a]

There are two other versions of this portrait in Cambridge, one in the Divinity School, dated 1896, and one at Gonville and Caius College, dated 1900. Both are replicas of an earlier original, presumably painted from the life but of unknown date, though in any case not before 1892 when he took the degree of Doctor of Letters.[b] As no fourth version is known, it may be that the present portrait is this original.

NOTES. (a) Letter in the College archives from (Sir) Arthur E. Shipley to the Master of Christ's College, Dr. Peile, dated 12 November 1900, stating the intention of buying the portrait. (b) See *Goodison*, pp. 66–7.

82   By A. T. PORTER

36 × $29\frac{1}{4}$ in. (91.4 × 74.6 cm.). Canvas. Half-length seated, turned, facing and looking slightly right, the right hand on an open book in his lap, the left arm resting supported at the right. Bare-headed, grey hair; clean-shaven. Over dark jacket and waistcoat with gold watch-chain, wears scarlet Litt.D. gown. Signed upper right, 'A.P.' in a monogram.

Probably acquired about 1907.[a]

Date unknown. He looks considerably younger than in no. **81** above, but, as with that portrait, this cannot be before 1892 on account of the doctor's gown he wears.

NOTE. (a) College Meetings, 30 November 1906, minute 16, and 18 January 1907, minute 8, from which it only appears that discussions were then proceeding about the portrait.

83   By G. MILNER-GIBSON-CULLUM

$5\frac{1}{4}$ × $3\frac{5}{8}$ in. (13.3 × 9.2 cm.). Pen and ink sketch. Whole-length standing, profile right, lecturing from a high desk. Bare-headed, bald, hair long at the back; clean-shaven. Wears academical gown. Seated figures slightly suggested in the background. Inscribed upper right, 'Seeley', upper left, 'c.1879–1880', below, 'by G. Milner-Gibson-Cullum/Trin. Coll. Cambs'.

Given by Sir Lionel H. Cust, K.C.V.O., 1923.[a]

Perhaps not a very exact portrait, as the two preceding ones show that he was not bald by 1892.

NOTE. (a) Letter in the College archives from Sir Lionel Cust to the Master of Christ's College, Sir Arthur E. Shipley, dated 16 July 1923, offering the sketch which he had found in going through the papers of his late friend G. Milner-Gibson-Cullum.

SHARP, JOHN

1645–1714. Admitted 1660, B.A. 1663/4, D.D. 1679. On Henry More's recommendation became domestic chaplain to Sir Heneage Finch, Solicitor General; later his adviser when Finch Lord Chancellor. Rector of St. Bartholomew Exchange, then St. Giles-in-the-Fields, London, retaining latter as Dean of Norwich despite criticism. Dean of Canterbury 1689–91; Archbishop of York 1691–1714. A famous preacher reputed for fair-mindedness. Refused to accept see vacated by non-jurors and helped distressed Scottish clergy, yet prayed for James II in 1689. [*D.N.B.; Peile*, i, 590; *Venn*, I.iv, 49].

84   Painter unknown

$47\frac{1}{2} \times 36\frac{1}{2}$ in. (120.6 × 92.6 cm.). Canvas. Half-length seated, turned and facing half left, looking front. Bare-headed, long light brown hair; clean-shaven. Wears rochet and chimere, with bands. The hands placed on a large book open on a green-covered table before him. In the background left the base of a column. Inscribed lower left, 'John Sharp. Arch-Bp. of York'.

Bought, 1922.[a] With Charles Newman, London, from whom it was bought.

NOTE. (a) College Meeting, 23 February 1922, minute 11.

SHIPLEY, SIR ARTHUR EVERETT

1861–1927. Admitted 1880, B.A. 1884, Sc.D. 1911. Fellow 1887, Reader in Zoology 1908, Tutor 1892, Master 1910–27, Vice-Chancellor 1917–19. Famous for both popular and academic work on parasites. A humorous lecturer and conversationalist. Thought highly of his college, restoring the Lodge at his own expense and contributing to the collection of Milton portraits. F.R.S. 1904, G.B.E. 1920. [*D.N.B. 1922–30; Peile*, ii, 673; *Venn*, II.v, 499].

85   By P. A. de LASZLO, 1925   PLATE IX

$32\frac{5}{8} \times 23\frac{1}{2}$ in. (82.8 × 59.7 cm.). Canvas. Half-length, turned half right, facing and looking front. Bare-headed, grey hair; moustache. Wears scarlet Vice-Chancellor's robe with white fur tippet, and bands. Signed and dated lower left, 'de László / 1925 July'.

Given by Sir Arthur E. Shipley, 1927.[a]

Painted to commemorate his tenure of the office of Vice-Chancellor of the University, 1917–19. The portrait was considered 'brilliantly successful' and was looked on by the painter as 'one of the best things he has done'.[b]

REPRODUCED. *Country Life*, lviii (1925), 529.

NOTES. (a) College Meeting, 29 April 1927, minute 5. (b) *Christ's College Magazine*, xxxiv (1926–7), 186.

86   By R. TAIT McKENZIE

Circular plaque, $10\frac{3}{8}$ in. diam. (26.7 cm.). Bronze. Head, turned, facing and looking profile left. Bare-headed; moustache. The jacket collar is partly seen below, over a high shirt collar with knotted tie. Inscribed round the margin, 'ARTHUR E · SHIPLEY · MAGISTER COLLEGII'. Signed below the figure,

'RTM', in a monogram; to right on a scroll the (Beaufort) motto 'SOUVENT ME SOUVIENT', with the College arms to right.[a]

Presumably bequeathed to Christ's College by Sir Arthur E. Shipley, 1927.

Perhaps modelled about 1922, when Tait McKenzie was occupied on the Cambridge War Memorial (see no. **39**).

NOTE. (a) The motto and arms are those of Lady Margaret Beaufort, the Foundress of Christ's College; the arms are: France modern quartering England within a bordure compony silver and azure.

SKEAT, WALTER WILLIAM

1835–1912. Admitted 1854, B.A. 1858, Litt.D. 1886. Fellow 1860, 1883–1916; ordained 1861; Professor of Anglo-Saxon 1878–1912. Editor of many early English texts, and an internationally known philologist. [*D.N.B. 1912–21; Peile*, ii, 534; *Venn*, II.v, 524].

87   By C. E. BROCK, 1899

$50\frac{1}{8} \times 39\frac{7}{8}$ in. (127.2 × 101.3 cm.). Canvas. To below knees seated, turned, facing and looking half right, elbows on the arms of his chair, hands clasped before him. Bare-headed, white hair; grey bushy beard and moustache. Wears black academical Litt.D. gown over black clothes. Signed and dated lower left, 'C. E. BROCK, 1899'.

Given by the subscribers, 1900.[a]

Painted for the subscribers to the Professor Skeat Portrait Fund, and presented to Skeat at the annual meeting of the Modern Language Association at London University, December 1899, to commemorate his presidency of the Association.[b] A replica was painted for Skeat's private possession, presumably thus releasing the original of 1899 for presentation to the College.

NOTES. (a) Letter in Christ's College archives from Israel Gollancz, 22 November 1900, offering it to the College on behalf of the subscribers; accepted at a College Meeting on 23 November 1900, Order 1. (b) *Christ's College Magazine*, xiv (1899–1900), 65; a circular of November 1899 appealing for subscriptions (Cambridge University Library, Cambridge Papers, no. BP 783) states that the purpose of the portrait was to recognise 'his many services to English Literature, and Modern Philology'.

SMITH, CHARLES LESINGHAM

1806–1878. Admitted 1825, B.A. 1829. Fellow 1830; ordained 1832; Rector of Little Canfield (Essex) 1839–78. A great collector of books, many of which left to College. [*Peile*, ii, 419; *Venn*, II.v, 545].

88   By HIRAM POWERS, 1845

Bust, 29 in. high (including base $5\frac{3}{8}$ in. high; 73.6 cm., base 13.6 cm.). White marble. Turned front, facing and looking slightly right. Bare-headed; side-whiskers meeting under the chin. Drapery falls across the front of the bust, leaving the throat bare. Signed at the back, 'HIRAM POWERS/Sculp.'.

Bequeathed by the Rev. Charles Lesingham Smith, 1878.[a] Exh. R.A., 1845 (1409).

NOTE. (a) Agreement Book, 25 October 1878, minute 3.

SMITH, WILLIAM ROBERTSON

1846–1894. Educated at Aberdeen, Edinburgh, Bonn and Göttingen; Professor of Oriental Languages and Old Testament in Free Church College, Aberdeen, 1870–81, Editor of *Encyclopaedia Britannica* 1881–8; Professor of Arabic 1883, Fellow of Christ's 1885, University Librarian 1886–9, Adams Professor of Arabic 1889–94. Left fine oriental books to the College. [*D.N.B.; Peile*, ii, 712; *Venn*, II.v, 575].

89   By SIR GEORGE REID, P.R.S.A.

$22\frac{1}{8} \times 31\frac{1}{8}$ in. (56.2 × 79.0 cm.). Canvas. To knees seated at a table covered with an oriental carpet, turned almost profile right, facing and looking half right. Bare-headed, bushy dark hair; dark moustache and slight beard. Wears black jacket and brown trousers. Holds a large book open on the edge of the table, on which, to right, are books and papers. Signed lower left with a monogram.

Bequeathed by Professor W. Robertson Smith, 1894, with a life interest to his mother, who died 1899, received 1900.[a] Exh. Royal Scottish Academy, 1877 (207).

In 1877 Professor Robertson Smith became a Fellow of the Royal Society of Edinburgh; another portrait of him by Sir George Reid was exhibited at the Royal Scottish Academy in 1880 (256), perhaps the one given as a memorial in 1895 to the Free Church College in Aberdeen.[b] The present portrait hung during his lifetime in his rooms in Christ's College.

NOTES. (a) Letter in the College archives, 8 March 1900, from Messrs. Yeats, Milner, McDonald of Aberdeen. (b) *Christ's College Magazine*, xi (1896–7), 72.

SMUTS, JAN CHRISTIAAN

1870–1950. Admitted 1891, B.A. 1894, LL.B. 1894. Offered and refused Fellowship 1895, Hon. Fellow 1915; Chancellor of the University 1948–50. Practised at Bar, Cape Town, 1894–96, then moved to the Transvaal, becoming in 1898 State Attorney. Opposed policy which led to South African War, but on outbreak took up arms, eventually becoming General with supreme command of Boer forces in Cape Colony. Took full responsibility for South African part in wars of 1914 and 1939, in both of which he played an important part in War Cabinet. Prime Minister of South Africa 1919–24, 1939–48. C.H. 1917, O.M. 1947. [*D.N.B. 1941–50; Peile*, ii, 771; *Venn*, II.v, 577].

90   By ARTHUR PAN

$29\frac{5}{8} \times 24\frac{3}{4}$ in. (75.2 × 65.4 cm.). Canvas. Nearly half-length, turned front, facing and looking half right, the glance somewhat raised, head inclined to his right. Bare-headed, grey hair; white chin beard and moustache. Wears khaki uniform with three rows of medal ribbons.

Commissioned by the College, 1944.

Replica painted by the artist in 1944 of a portrait he painted probably in 1942, now at South Africa House, London. There were no sittings for the original, which was painted from memory with the aid of a photograph of Smuts in the same pose. It is understood that the original was greatly liked by Smuts, though he considered the mouth unduly hard. The replica was commissioned as Smuts was unable to give sittings for a fresh portrait for the College during a visit to London in May and June 1944.

REPRODUCED. *Christ's College Magazine,* xlix (1944–5), 57.

91   By PRINCE BIRABONGSE, 1943

Head, 19 in. high (including base $7\frac{7}{8}$ in. high; 48.2 cm., base 20.0 cm.). Bronze. Facing and looking front. Bare-headed, receding hair; moustache and chin beard. Signed and dated at the back, 'BIRA 43'.

Given jointly by H.H. Prince Birabongse and H.R.H. Chula Chakrabongse, G.C.V.O., 1953.[a]

Modelled in Cornwall, where the sculptor was working, from photographs.[b]

NOTES. (a) College Meeting, 16 June 1953, minute 5, and information from Prince Chula Chakrabongse. Prince Birabongse was the nephew of King Chulalongkorn of Thailand, and cousin of Prince Chula. (b) Information from Prince Chula Chakrabongse.

SWAINSON, CHARLES ANTHONY

1820–1887. B.A. (Trinity) 1841, D.D. 1864. Fellow of Christ's 1841–52. Principal, Theological College, Chichester, 1854–64; Norrisian Professor of Divinity 1864–79; Lady Margaret Professor 1879–87. Master of Christ's 1881–7. Vice-Chancellor 1885–6. Historian of the creeds. [*D.N.B.; Peile*, ii, 461; *Venn*, II.vi, 89].

92   By EDWIN WILSON, 1901

$8 \times 6\frac{1}{4}$ in. (20.3 × 15.8 cm.). Brush and Indian ink, (?) with pencil. Head and shoulders, turned, facing and looking half left. Bare-headed, bald; side-whiskers meeting under the chin; spectacles. Wears clerical dress. Signed and dated lower right, 'Edwin Wilson. Mar. 1901'.

Source of acquisition unknown.

Posthumous portrait after an unknown original.

SWANN, SAMUEL KIRKE

*c.*1816–1886. Admitted 1838, B.A. 1842. Curate of Gedling (Notts.) 1853–86. Did much voluntary work. [*Peile*, ii, 463; *Venn*, II.vi, 93].

93   By CANON G. F. WESTON

$5\frac{1}{4} \times 4$ in. (13.3 × 10.1 cm.). Pencil. Half-length, seated in an upholstered arm-chair, turned, facing and looking three-quarters left, hands resting in his lap. Bare-headed; clean-shaven. Wears jacket with high collar and stock.

Given by Mrs. C. W. Benson, daughter of Canon Weston, 1923.[a]

Probably drawn by Canon Weston while an undergraduate at Christ's College, 1840-44. See also nos. **5, 33, 34, 40, 48, 51, 69, 79, 94, 96, 100.**

NOTE. (a) College Meeting, 15 March 1923, minute 12.

TANCRED, D'ARCY

Born *c.*1817. Admitted 1837, B.A. 1842. Educated for Holy Orders. [*Peile,* ii, 459; *Venn,* II.vi, 108].

94 By CANON G. F. WESTON

$5\frac{1}{4}$ × 4 in. (13.3 × 10.1 cm.). Pencil. To knees seated, turned, facing and looking nearly profile left, hands clasped in his lap. Bare-headed, dark hair; clean-shaven. Wears jacket and waistcoat with high collar and stock.

Given by Mrs. C. W. Benson, daughter of Canon Weston, 1923.[a]

Probably drawn by Canon Weston while an undergraduate at Christ's College, 1840-44. See also nos. **5, 33, 34, 40, 48, 51, 69, 79, 93, 96, 100.**

NOTE. (a) College Meeting, 15 March 1923, minute 12.

TODD of Trumpington, ALEXANDER ROBERTUS TODD, first Baron

Born 1907. University of Glasgow Carnegie Research Scholar 1928-9. Subsequent appointments in universities of Glasgow, Frankfurt am Main, Oxford, Edinburgh, London and Manchester. Professor of Organic Chemistry, University of Cambridge, 1944-71. Fellow of Christ's College 1944-63, Master 1963-78. Biochemist noted for work on nucleic acids. Royal medal of Royal Society 1955, Nobel prize for chemistry 1957. F.R.S. 1942 (President 1975-80). Knighted 1954, Life Peer 1962, O.M. 1977. Many academic and professional appointments and distinctions. (First) Chancellor, University of Strathclyde, Glasgow, 1964-. [*Who's Who*].

95 By ANNA ZINKEISEN

$44\frac{3}{4}$ × $36\frac{5}{8}$ in. (112.7 × 93.1 cm.). Canvas. Three-quarter length seated, turned and facing three-quarters left, looking half left. Bare-headed, grey hair; clean-shaven. Wears doctor's scarlet academical gown and hood. (Sc.D. University of Glasgow); hands clasped in his lap. Signed lower right, 'A. Zinkeisen'.

Commissioned by Christ's College 1959, completed 1960.

A smaller replica was a gift from Christ's College to the sitter.

VAUGHAN, EDWYN HENRY

1818-1868. Admitted 1838, B.A. 1842. Assistant Master, Harrow, where his brother was Headmaster. [*Peile,* ii, 463; *Venn,* II.vi, 279].

96 By CANON G. F. WESTON

$5\frac{1}{4}$ × 4 in. (13.3 × 10.1 cm.). Pencil. Half-length seated, turned, facing and looking half right, hands clasped in his lap. Bare-headed; clean-shaven but for side-whiskers. Wears jacket and waistcoat with high collar and stock.

Given by Mrs. C. W. Benson, daughter of Canon Weston, 1923.[a]

Probably drawn by Canon Weston while an undergraduate at Christ's College, 1840–44. See also nos. **5, 33, 34, 40, 48, 51, 69, 79, 93, 94, 100**.

NOTE. (a) College Meeting, 15 March 1923, minute 12.

WALL, ADAM

1728–1798. Born Cambridge, son of local apothecary; admitted 1746, B.A. 1750/1. Fellow 1756, Praelector, Junior Dean & Steward 1760; Senior Fellow from 1783. Biblical scholar who also organised college muniments. [*Peile*, ii, 249; *Venn*, I.iv, 320].

97   Artist unknown

Silhouette, $3\frac{5}{8} \times 3$ in. (9.2 × 7.6 cm.). Black ink. Head and shoulders, profile right. Bare-headed, wig; clean-shaven.

Source of acquisition unknown.

WARD, HARRY MARSHALL

1854–1906. Admitted 1877, B.A. 1880, Fellow 1883. After graduation pursued mycological research at Strasburg, Würzburg and in Ceylon. Fellow of Owens College, Manchester, 1882; Professor of Botany, Royal Indian Engineering College, 1885–95; Professor of Botany, Cambridge, 1895–1906. Fellow of Sidney Sussex and Hon. Fellow of Christ's 1897; Fellow of Linnean Society 1886. F.R.S. 1888. President of British Mycological Society 1900–2. [*D.N.B. 1901–1911; Peile*, ii, 655; *Venn*, II.vi, 343].

98   Artist unknown

$16\frac{1}{4} \times 12\frac{3}{8}$ in. (41.3 × 31.4 cm.), pastel. Bust, turned, facing and looking three-quarters left. Bare-headed, dark hair; long dark moustache. Over black clothes with wing collar and white bow tie, wears scarlet gown of a Cambridge Doctor of Science. Signed lower left in a monogram, 'CGD'.

Source of acquisition unknown.

It seems most likely that the letters of the monogram should be read in the order C,G,D, but attempts to elucidate them in each possible order have been unsuccessful. Perhaps the drawing is the work of an amateur. It cannot be earlier than 1892, the year in which he became an honorary Sc.D. of Cambridge.

WARD, SETH

1617–1689. Admitted Sidney Sussex College 1632, B.A. 1636/7, D.D. (Oxon.) 1654. Fellow of Sidney Sussex 1640, deprived 1644. Savilian Professor of Astronomy, Oxford, 1649–60. One of the 'Philosophical Society of Oxford', an antecedent of The Royal Society. President of Trinity College, Oxford, 1659–60. Dean of Exeter 1661, Bishop 1662–7. Bishop of Salisbury 1667–89. Mathematician and astronomer who beautified Exeter and Salisbury Cathedrals. A stern opponent of nonconformity. [*D.N.B.; Venn*, I.i, 334; *N.C.B.E.L.*, i, 2003].

99 By JOHN GREENHILL

$47\frac{1}{2} \times 37\frac{1}{2}$ in. (120.6 × 95.2 cm.). Canvas. Three-quarter length seated, turned and facing half left, looking front, the right arm resting on two books on a table left, the left hand on his knee. Black skull-cap over long brown hair; thin line of moustache. Wears mantle of Chancellor of the Order of the Garter over rochet and chimere with broad band-collar, the badge of the Order on a double gold chain hanging round his neck, the purse resting in his lap. A wall behind the figure ends to the left in a column, beyond which is a view of Salisbury Cathedral. Top right, his arms,[a] with the inscription below them 'SETH WARD Bp of SALISBURY 1667'.

Bought 1883, Coll. Robert Plumer Ward (1765–1846), Gilston Park, Hertfordshire;[b] perhaps his posthumous sale, Gilston Park, April 1851; with Mrs. Noseda, London, 1872; with the Rev. F. O. White, from whom it was bought.

A repetition probably by Greenhill of an original commissioned from him by the Corporation of Salisbury in 1673,[c] now in the Guildhall, Salisbury. Other versions are at Trinity College, Oxford, and in the County Record Office, Hertford, a modern copy is in the Bishop's Palace, Salisbury, and a head and shoulders copy is at Wadham College, Oxford. An engraved portrait of Ward by Loggan, inscribed 'D. Loggan ad vivum delin. et sculp. 1678', follows the Greenhill painting so closely as to suggest some degree of dependence upon it. In 1667 Ward became Bishop of Salisbury.

NOTES. (a) Azure a cross flory or; crest, a wolf's head argent on a wreath of the colours, azure and or. (b) His family, of Northwood, Isle of Wight, bore the same arms as the family of Bishop Seth Ward, but their genealogy is unknown before 1704. On his marriage to Jane Lewin, whose first husband was William Plumer of Gilston Park, he assumed the name of Plumer Ward. (c) Sir Harold Williams, 'Portraits of Seth Ward', *Transactions of the East Hertfordshire Archaeological Society*, xiii (1950–4), 9–12 (pl. 2 reproduces the version in the County Record Office, Hertford; that at Trinity College, Oxford, is reproduced on pl. XVI of the *Illustrated catalogue of a loan collection of portraits . . . Oxford*, 1905).

WESTON, THOMAS WOODS

1816–1891. Admitted Fellow-commoner 1847, LL.B. 1853. Vicar of St. John's Tunbridge Wells, 1858–91. [*Peile*, ii, 501; *Venn*, II.vi, 415].

100 By CANON G. F. WESTON

$5\frac{1}{4} \times 4$ in. (13.3 × 10.1 cm.). Pencil. Half-length seated, turned, facing and looking nearly profile right, left hand on back of chair, right hand on a book. Bare-headed, dark hair; clean-shaven but for side-whiskers. Wears jacket and waistcoat with high collar and stock.

Given by Mrs. C. W. Benson, daughter of Canon Weston, 1923.[a]

Younger brother of Canon Weston. Since he was not admitted at Christ's College until 1847, and it seems likely that the other portrait drawings by his elder brother (see nos. **5, 33, 34, 40, 48, 51, 69, 79, 93, 94, 96**) were done while he was an undergraduate there from 1840 to 1844, this may have been drawn at another time.

NOTE. (a) College Meeting, 15 March 1923, minute 12.

UNKNOWN MAN, later seventeenth century

101 Painter unknown

$21\frac{3}{8} \times 27\frac{1}{2}$ in. (54.2 × 69.8 cm.). Canvas. Half-length, turned and facing half right, looking front. Bare-headed, brown periwig; clean-shaven. Brown drapery; bands. Within a painted oval. Lower right, inscribed or (?) signed, 'GdS'.

Bought, 1883.[a] Perhaps coll. Rev. Robert Ainslie, London, 1859; with the Rev. F. O. White, from whom it was bought.[b]

Bought as a portrait of Ralph Cudworth, Master of Christ's College, 1654–88, but the identification cannot be accepted as correct. A drawing of him by D. Loggan of 1684, formerly to be found in the College, was engraved by G. Vertue as the frontispiece to Cudworth's *A treatise concerning eternal and immutable morality*, 1731,[c] and shows a man quite different in both appearance and character. The face in the engraving is square and full, instead of angular and lined, the character, vividly revealed in pose as well as expression, withdrawn, precise and fastidious, instead of active, shrewd and rather coarse. The difference is complete and cannot be accounted for on grounds of age. It has been tentatively suggested that the painter might be John Hayls.[d] The characters towards the lower right corner, interpreted above as 'GdS', seem unlikely to be a signature.

NOTES. (a) Agreement Book, 1860–95, 6 February 1883, minute 4. (b) See note (b) to no. **63**. (c) William Cole in 1749 says of drawing and engraving, 'There is a very neat *octavo Print* of him done from a *Pencil Drawing* now in the *Master's Lodge* at *Christ's College*, from whence *M*[r]. *Vertue* did it: ... both which represent him in a *long black Wig* and *Scull Cap* and in his *Canonical Habit*' (British Library, Add. MS. 5821, Cole's 'Various collections for Cambridgeshire', vol. XX, fol. 74). The drawing was still in the College in the time of Masters (p. 28). (d) By J. D. Milner, see *Christ's College Magazine*, xxvi (1911–12), 16.

UNKNOWN YOUNG WOMAN, *circa* 1680

102 Painter unknown, probably English

$18\frac{1}{2} \times 15\frac{3}{4}$ in. (47.0 × 40.0 cm.). Canvas. Bust length, turned and facing half left, eyes to front; high complexion. Wears a black widow's bonnet, with a peak over the forehead; dark brown hair in ringlets, two long curls falling over her left shoulder. An oval and a crescent-shaped black patch beside her left eye. Wears a black dress off the shoulders, which are covered by transparent white material, fastened down the front with laces ending in tassels.

Given by the executors of Professor Torkel Weis-Fogh (d.1975).

Considerably damaged by over-cleaning. The date may be deduced from the costume and hair-style. Given as a portrait of Charlotte Corday (1763–1798).

CLARE COLLEGE

Clare College owes the portrait of its Foundress (no. **107**) to the antiquarian interest in portraiture which developed in the course of the eighteenth century, but in this case, unfortunately, with no basis in a contemporary original. Of the eight painted portraits listed by *Masters* in about 1790, which may include the fine Kneller of Bishop Moore of 1705 (no. **126**), all still hang in the College, but none has a recorded origin. Until modern times the identity of the painters of the portraits is seldom known, but among the exceptions a distinguished example, besides the Kneller already mentioned, is the portrait of Isaac Bargrave (no. **105**) by Cornelius Johnson, 1636, a purchase of 1933. The prevailing fog of ignorance about the acquisition of portraits, is happily dispelled in the case of the benefactions of the Rev. H. J. Carter who, between 1892 and 1899, gave six, or possibly seven, portraits (nos. **108, 111, 115, 118, 120, 136**; possible, no. **122**). Before comparatively modern times, only one portrait of a Master of the College is to be found, that of Peter Stephen Godard, Master 1762–81 (no. **116**), though not an early acquisition. From the time of William Webb, Master 1815–56 (no. **138**), portraits of Masters form a continuous series to that of Lord Ashby.

ASHBY of Brandon, ERIC ASHBY, first Baron

Born 1904. Educated at City of London School and London University. Botanist and author. Held academic posts in London, Chicago, Bristol, Sydney, and Manchester, 1926–50. President and Vice-Chancellor, Queen's University, Belfast, 1950–59. Knighted, 1956. F.R.S. A member of numerous societies and recipient of many honorary degrees. Fellow of the College and M.A. 1958; Master, 1959–75; Life Fellow, 1975. Vice-Chancellor, 1967–9. Chancellor of Queen's University, Belfast, since 1970. Created life peer, 1973. [*Who's Who*]

103 By BRYAN ORGAN, 1975

$59\frac{3}{4} \times 59\frac{3}{4}$ in. (151.8 × 151.8 cm.). Acrylic on canvas. Half-length, seated to front, right hand on chair arm, left hand in front. Bare-headed, bald, clean-shaven; spectacles. Grey suit, with a white shirt and red tie. Behind, the buff-coloured steps of a building rise from left and right, with dark grey railings, a black doorway behind the head. Signed and dated lower right, 'Bryan Organ 1975'.

Commissioned by the College, 1975. Exh. London, Redfern Gallery, 1975, 'Bryan Organ' (10).

Commissioned during Lord Ashby's final year as Master of the College.

REPRODUCED. *Clare Association Annual 1974–5*, frontispiece.

ATKINSON, EDWARD

1819–1915. Admitted sizar, 1838; later scholar. B.A. 1842; M.A. 1845; B.D. 1853; D.D. 1859. Fellow, 1842. Tutor and lecturer in classics. Master of the College, 1856–1915, and Vice-Chancellor, 1862, 1868, 1869, 1876, 1877. Ordained deacon, 1844; priest, 1846. Fellow of Winchester College, 1875–90. Benefactor to the College Library. His tenure of the Mastership was the longest in the history of the University. [*Venn*, II.i, 92]

104 By W. W. OULESS, R.A., 1906

$35\frac{5}{8} \times 27\frac{1}{2}$ in. (90.5 × 69.8 cm.). Long half-length, seated, nearly in profile right, reading, a book held up before him in both hands. Bare-headed, grey hair; grey beard and moustache. Wears black academical gown over dark clothes, scarlet hood of Doctor of Divinity. Signed and dated lower right, 'Walter W. Ouless/1906'.

Source of acquisition unknown. Exh. R.A. 1906 (88).

In 1906 Atkinson completed his fiftieth year as Master of Clare College, and upon the occasion an address of congratulation was presented to him by the Council of the Senate of the University. The painting of the portrait is evidently connected with this anniversary, but no details of how it came about appear to have been recorded.

REPRODUCED. *Royal Academy illustrated* (1906), 78; M. D. Forbes, *Clare College*, i (1928), 192, pl. XXVI.

BARGRAVE, ISAAC

1586-1643. B.A. (Pembroke) 1606-7, M.A. 1610; D.D. (Clare) 1621. University Taxor and Fellow of Clare, 1612, in which year he was ordained. Rector of Eythorne (Kent) 1614-42; Rector of St. Margaret's, Westminster, 1622, and holder of other benefices. Dean of Canterbury, 1625-43. Author of sermons. He became very unpopular with the clergy and was briefly imprisoned in 1642. Buried in Canterbury Cathedral where a memorial was erected in 1679. Described by Izaak Walton as 'learned and hospitable'. [D.N.B.; Venn, I.i, 84]

105 By CORNELIUS JOHNSON, 1636   PLATE IV

31 × 24¾ in. (78.7 × 62.9 cm.). Canvas. Half-length seated, turned and facing half right, looking front. Bare-headed, dark brown hair; dark brown moustache and beard. Wears black silk robe like a cassock, with plain white collar. In his left hand holds an armorial seal. Signed and dated lower right, 'CJ/ 1636'.

Bought 1933. (?) Coll. C. E. Gunther, d.1931;[a] (?) Christie's, Anon. (= Leggatt Bros.), 26 May 1933 (43);[b] with David Minlore, London, from whom it was bought.

Another example of this portrait was (1947) in the possession of Mrs. Noel Russell. A variant by Johnson, unsigned, in different dress and holding the seal in the right hand, is in the Deanery, Canterbury, a second example of which is inset in a wall monument to the memory of Bargrave, erected in 1679, in the chapel of the Virgin Mary, Canterbury Cathedral. Another portrait by Johnson, of unknown type, on wood, outside dimensions of the frame 36½ × 45½ in. (92.7 × 115.6 cm.), belonged (1933) to Miss N. M. H. Dodge, Hove.

REPRODUCED. *Connoisseur*, cxl (1957), 231.

NOTES. (a) *Walpole Society*, x (1922), 28, no. 77, rep. pl. LIII, corresponding in composition and signed the same, but the dimensions are given as 29 × 24 in. (73.6 × 60.9 cm.). (b) On canvas, dimensions 31 × 25 in. (78.7 × 63.5 cm.), catalogued as 'C. Johnson 1636', but no signature or date noted; the Clare College portrait bears no Christie stencil on the back.

BUTLER, WILLIAM

1535-1618. Matriculated sizar from Peterhouse, 1557-8; B.A. 1560-1; M.A. 1564. The details of his career are obscure on account of the commonness of the name; a William Butler was a Fellow of Clare from 1564 to 1581. He obtained a licence to practise medicine and styled himself 'Doctor'. Well known in Cambridge for his skill and eccentricity. He attended Henry, Prince of Wales, in his final illness, 1612. Benefactor. [D.N.B.; Venn, I.i, 274]

106 Painter unknown, early seventeenth century

21¾ × 17⅛ in. (55.2 × 43.5 cm.). Wood. Half-length, turned and facing half right, looking front. Wears embroidered, gold-coloured close round cap; grey beard and moustache. Black dress with flat, pleated ruff with strings. In his right hand he holds a quill pen as though writing.

Source of acquisition unknown. *Masters* p. 23, no. 1; exh. C.A.S. 1885 (13).

Much damaged and repaired. An engraving by Simon van de Passe, dated 1620, is very similar to this in reverse,[a] the (left) hand resting on a book instead of holding a pen.

ENGRAVED. By Clamp after Silvester Harding, 'From an Original Picture in Clare Hall, Cambridge'.[b]

NOTES. (a) A. M. Hind, *Engraving in England in the sixteenth and seventeenth centuries*, ii (1955), 253, no. 14, pl. 149(a). (b) In *Harding's biographical mirrour*, ii (1795), no. 5.

CLARE, LADY ELIZABETH DE

1291(?)–1360. Daughter of Gilbert, ninth Earl of Clare, and his second wife Joan, daughter of Edward I. A considerable heiress who survived three husbands. Became 'Lady of Clare' on the death of her brother at Bannockburn in 1314. In 1336 she endowed University Hall (afterwards called Clare Hall), and framed statutes for it in 1359. [*D.N.B.*]

107 Copy by JOSEPH FREEMAN

$49\frac{1}{4} \times 39\frac{1}{4}$ in. (125.1 × 99.7 cm.). Canvas. Three-quarter length standing, turned and facing half right, looking front. A white veil falls from the headdress; she wears a black dress edged with ermine over a white chemise, a jewel on a ribbon round her neck. In her right hand she holds a book against her abdomen, the left is placed on her breast.

Source of acquisition unknown. *Masters* p. 24, no. 9.

This corresponds with the mezzotint by John Faber sen., dated 1714, which is no. 16 in his *Fundatores Collegiorum Cantabrigiensum.*[a] Though Faber describes these engravings as 'from the original paintings in Cambridge', when no such portraits existed it is apparent that he supplied them, if necessary from his own invention. This is the case with his mezzotint of the Lady Elizabeth de Clare. Her tomb, if it had an effigy, was destroyed in the sixteenth century,[b] and Faber invented this imaginary figure, clad in a fancy costume which bears no relation to that of the fourteenth or any other century.[c] It is not surprising that oil-paintings were made, copied from such engravings, to supply the deficiency of a founder's portrait. Such is the present one, in the same direction as the engraving, described by *Masters* about 1790 as 'Copy by Freeman',[d] presumably the Joseph Freeman who in 1776 was employed by the University for cleaning pictures and repairing frames in the University Library.[e] There seems no doubt that this, and not the next portrait of the Lady Elizabeth de Clare, is to be identified with that listed by *Masters*, since he describes it as '½ length', the equivalent of a three-quarter length in present terminology. All but the head was badly damaged, perhaps in the fire of 1890.

ENGRAVED. R. Ackermann, *History of Cambridge* (1815), p. 26.

NOTES. (a) J. Chaloner Smith, *British mezzotinto portraits*, Part I (1878), p. 277, no. 34, and p. 282. (b) J. R. Wardale, *Clare College* (1899), p. 212. (c) It may be noted that Faber sometimes states in the inscription on his mezzotints that they are taken from a painting in the College, but that he does not do so in this case. (d) Page 24, no. 9. (e) *Goodison*, p. 3, note (a) to Colet.

108 Painter unknown

$29\frac{3}{8} \times 18\frac{3}{4}$ in. (74.7 × 47.7 cm.), oval. Canvas. Half-length, turned and facing half right, looking front. A white veil falls from the head-dress; she wears a black dress edged with ermine over a white chemise, a jewel on a ribbon round her neck. In her right hand she carries a book, the left is placed on her breast.

Given by the Rev. H. J. Carter, 1899.[a]

This is a reduced copy of no. **107** above.

NOTE. (a) College Order Book, 3 November 1899.

COLES, THOMAS HENRY

*c.*1783–1867. Admitted pensioner, 1799; B.A. 1803; M.A. 1806; D.D. 1818. Ordained priest, 1805. Vicar of Honington (Lincs.), 1805–67. Gave an organ and nine windows to the Chapel. Bequeathed his whole estate to the College subject to a life interest. From this the Coles Scholarships and two Fellowships were founded. [*Venn*, II.ii, 93]

109 Painter unknown

$29\frac{3}{8} \times 24\frac{3}{8}$ in. (74.6 × 61.9 cm.). Canvas. Half-length, turned and facing half right, looking front, leaning with his left arm on a table right, a pamphlet in the hand, finger between the leaves. Bare-headed, dark brown curly hair; clean-shaven, ruddy complexion. Wears black dress with black academical gown, choker and jabot frill. Shelves of books in the background, covered by a red curtain behind the figure.

Source of acquisition unknown.[a]

The gown he wears is that of a Master of Arts, a degree he took in 1806. Supposing he was aged about eighteen on admission in 1799, the portrait could well be of about the date of his M.A. degree, to judge from his apparent age of about twenty-five.

NOTE. (a) As it is not listed in *Atkinson and Clark* (1897) it presumably came after this date, possibly as a gift or bequest from the widow of T. H. Coles's son, the Rev. Henry Apreece Coles, who died in 1882, and left all his pictures to his wife Charlotte. Apart from an annuity to his son, T. H. Coles bequeathed to Clare College the whole of his estate.

COOPER, BRIAN

Born 1911. Admitted exhibitioner, 1929. B.A. 1932; M.A. 1936. In industry, 1932–6. Lecturer, King's College, London, 1937–8; University Demonstrator in Engineering and later Lecturer, 1938–78. Fellow of the College since 1944 and Bursar, 1949–78.

110 By JOHN WARD, R.A., 1979

$14\frac{1}{8} \times 18\frac{7}{8}$ in. (35.9 × 48.0 cm.). Black chalk and water-colour. To knees, seated, turned half left, in his College rooms, reading the *Financial Times*. Bare-headed, clean-shaven, spectacles. Light brown jacket and trousers; patterned tie; light blue shirt. Signed and dated lower right, 'John Ward 1979'.

Commissioned by the College, 1978.

Good likeness.

CORNWALLIS, CHARLES CORNWALLIS, first Marquess

1738–1805. Admitted nobleman 1755. Served in the army on the continent and later in America, 1776–81. Succeeded as Earl Cornwallis 1762; created marquess 1792. Governor-General of Bengal 1786–93 and 1805; Commander-in-Chief in the East Indies 1786–93. Lord-Lieutenant of Ireland 1798–1801, assisting in the Union. Signed the treaty of Amiens, 1802. Died in India. [*D.N.B.*; *Venn*, II.ii, 140; studies by A. Aspinall (1931), and F. & M. Wickwire (1971)]

111 By LANCELOT SPEED, 1890, after J. S. COPLEY[a]

$59\frac{1}{2} \times 49\frac{1}{2}$ in. (151.1 × 125.7 cm.). Canvas. Three-quarter length standing, turned slightly left, facing and looking slightly right. Bare-headed, wig; clean-shaven. Wears scarlet uniform jacket with dark blue facings and gold epaulettes, with white waistcoat and buff breeches, star and riband of the Garter. Right hand rests on a cane, the left on a bank. Background to left a landscape with cantonment buildings.

Given by the Rev. H. J. Carter, 1892.[b]

The original by J. S. Copley is at Guildhall, London, the gift of Alderman John Boydell in 1793.[c] In 1792 Marquess Cornwallis was presented with the Freedom of the City of London 'in a gold box', an event with which the portrait is evidently connected.[d] Another copy by S. Lane is at the Oriental Club, London.

NOTES. (a) A. G. Temple, *Catalogue of the works of art belonging to the Corporation of London* (1910), p. 50, no. 59. (b) College Order Book, 11 February 1892, minute 4. (c) Temple, *loc. cit.* (d) Temple, *loc. cit.*

CRESSWELL, FRANCIS

1762?–1841. Admitted sizar, 1780; later scholar. B.A. 1785; M.A. 1788; B.D. 1796. Fellow, 1785. Tutor. Ordained priest, 1792. Vicar of Duxford St. John (Cambs.), 1797–1806; Rector of Great Waldingfield (Suffolk), 1807–41. [*Venn*, II.ii, 176]

112 Painter unknown

$16\frac{3}{8} \times 13\frac{1}{2}$ in. (41.6 × 34.3 cm.). Canvas. Half-length, turned and facing half right, looking front. Bare-headed, fair, curly receding hair; clean-shaven, fresh warm complexion. Over black dress with high collar wears black academical gown. Red curtain behind the figure.

Given by Sir Dennis Herbert, K.B.E., (?) 1937.

From his appearance he might be in the early forties, giving a date early in the nineteenth century. Of mediocre quality.

EXETER, THOMAS CECIL, first Earl of

1542–1623. Eldest son of William, Lord Burghley. Matriculated Fellow Commoner from Trinity, 1558; M.A. 1571. M.P. for Stamford etc. Knighted, 1575. Prominent in military campaigns in Scotland and the Low Countries. President of the Council of the North, 1599. K.G. 1601. Created Earl of Exeter, 1605. Benefactor. [*D.N.B.*; *Venn*, I.i, 313]

113 Painter unknown, earlier seventeenth century   PLATE II

$82\frac{1}{2} \times 46\frac{5}{8}$ in. (209.6 × 118.4 cm.). Canvas. Whole-length standing, turned and facing quarter left, looking front. Wears tall black hat, grey hair; grey moustache and chin beard. Long black gown, furred and gold-laced, over black dress, with the Greater George of the Garter on a blue riband, the Garter round his left knee. Grey gloves, a stick in his right hand. Beneath his feet an oriental carpet; behind, at either side, looped pink silk curtains.

Source of acquisition unknown. In the College by 1721/22;[a] *Masters* p. 24, no. 10.

Another version of this portrait is at Hatfield House (Marquess of Salisbury, formerly at Woburn Abbey, Duke of Bedford),[b] in which he stands before a more elaborate background and wears a gown without gold lace; on the carpet to left lies a paper inscribed 'Thomas Earle of Exeter/eldest son to Lord/Treasurer Burghley', thus giving a *terminus a quo* for the portrait of 1605, the year in which he was created Earl of Exeter. A date of 1612 has been given for the Hatfield portrait, but without supporting evidence,[c] though the costume is of about this date. It was in 1612, when he became seventy, that he endowed Clare College with an annuity of £108 for the creation of three fellowships and eight scholarships.[d] The Hatfield portrait has been associated with the work of Marcus Gheeraerts,[e] but neither it nor the Cambridge version resembles his known authentic paintings. A half-length version of the Hatfield portrait is at Burghley House (Marquess of Exeter). These three pictures represent the only identifiable portrait-type of Exeter.[f]

NOTES. (a) College Audit Book, Michaelmas 1721–Michaelmas 1722, Expensae Generales, 'P.d M.r Rix for mending the L.d Exeter's Picture 03 03 00. Ditto for a new Frame and Carriage 04 09 00'. 'M.r Rix' was Valentine Ritz, a painter resident in Cambridge, see *Goodison*, p. 8, note (b) to no. 8. (b) Rep. *Walpole Society*, iii (1914), pl. XXXVIII. (c) Anon. (Wiffen), *A descriptive catalogue of the portraits in the collection of John, Duke of Bedford, K.G., at Woburn Abbey* (1836), no. CCLXXII. (d) J. R. Wardale, *Clare College* (1899), p. 99. (e) By Lionel Cust, *Walpole Society*, iii (1914), 33. (f) Roy Strong, *Tudor and Jacobean portraits* (National Portrait Gallery, 1969), i, 118.

FERRAR, NICHOLAS

1593–1637. B.A. 1609–10; Fellow 1610; perhaps M.A. 1613, in which year he accompanied the Queen of Bohemia to Holland. Involved in the Virginia Company and travelled widely. M.P. for Lymington 1624–5. Retired to Little Gidding (Hunts.) in 1625 and was ordained by Laud in 1626. Founded at Gidding a famous Anglican devotional community which survived him until 1647. [*D.N.B.*; *Venn*, I.ii, 134; *N.C.B.E.L.*, i, 1975–6; M. D. Forbes, *Clare College*, ii (1930), 389–586]

114 By W. M. HAY, 1867,[a] after (?) CORNELIUS JOHNSON

$35\frac{1}{2} \times 27\frac{1}{2}$ in. (90.2 × 69.8 cm.). Canvas. Half-length standing, turned and facing quarter right, looking front. Bare-headed, dark brown hair; dark brown moustache and imperial. Black dress, with white, folded, falling ruff-collar, and similar cuffs. Left hand on hip, right hand on bosom.

Source of acquisition unknown.[b]

Copy of the original at Magdalene College, the damaged condition of which has been faithfully rendered. Portraits of his mother and father, Nicholas and Mary Ferrar, also at Magdalene, are by the same hand; both are dated 1617, which could be the date also of this portrait, though his apparent age is difficult to guess at with much confidence in the damaged state of the picture. In his copy of *Masters* in the Fitzwilliam Museum, Thomas Kerrich has noted that the portraits of Nicholas and Mary Ferrar are by Cornelius Johnson, but not that of their son, though all three appear to be by the same hand.

NOTES. (a) From a note on the back of the canvas. (b) Listed by *Atkinson and Clark* in 1897 as 'a recent copy' (p. 310), and thus perhaps one of the gifts of the Rev. H. J. Carter, who presented a number of copies of portraits to the College between 1892 and 1899.

FOLKES, MARTIN

1690–1754. Admitted Fellow-Commoner 1706; matriculated 1709; M.A. 1717. Studied at Saumur. D.C.L. Oxford 1746, incorporated at Cambridge 1749. Fellow and President of the Royal Society and President of the Society of Antiquaries. Author, antiquarian, especially numismatics. Monument erected in Westminster Abbey 1792. [*D.N.B.*; *Venn*, I.ii, 155]

115 By ROBERT FARREN after W. HOGARTH

$29\frac{1}{2} \times 24\frac{3}{8}$ in. (74.9 × 61.9 cm.). Canvas. Half-length, turned, facing and looking quarter left. Bare-headed, brown wig; clean-shaven. Brown jacket and waistcoat. To lower left is seen his right hand with the first finger extended pointing, a frill of shirt cuff encircling the wrist.

Given by the Rev. H. J. Carter, 1895.[a]

The original by Hogarth belongs to the Royal Society, London, to which it was given by Folkes in 1742; it is said to have been painted in 1741, the year in which he became President.[b] The Rev. H. J. Carter gave a number of copies of portraits to the College in the eighteen-nineties.

NOTES. (a) From a label at the back, which gives also the name of the copyist. (b) R. B. Beckett, *Hogarth* (1941), p. 50, rep. pl. 133.

GODARD, PETER STEPHEN

1705-1781. Admitted sizar, 1721; B.A. 1724-5; M.A. 1728; D.D. 1761. Fellow, 1727; Senior Proctor, 1745-6; Master, 1762-81; Vice-Chancellor, 1762-3. Ordained priest 1730, and held livings in East Anglia. Prebendary of Peterborough 1761-81, and of St. Paul's 1770-81. Author, sermons. [*Venn*, I.ii, 226]

116 (?) By JOHN DOWNMAN

29 x 24 in. (73.7 x 60.9 cm.). Canvas. Half-length, turned, facing and looking nearly profile left. Bare-headed, grey cauliflower wig; clean-shaven. Wears scarlet academical gown with black scarf and bands. Background a landscape, with a low horizon at the left, trees and a dark sky.

(?) Given or bequeathed by Edward Atkinson, Master of Clare College from 1856 to his death in 1915. Coll. (?) John Mortlock, Cambridge, and his great friend Gilbert Ainslie, Master of Pembroke College; Henry Latham, Master of Trinity Hall, who gave it to Dr. Atkinson shortly before his death in 1902.

This corresponds with a drawing in the Fitzwilliam Museum (no. 1852) by John Downman, dated 1777 and inscribed 'painted large as Life for John Mortlock Esqr'.[a] From a certain feebleness of quality, some doubt may be felt of this being Downman's original painting.

NOTE (a) See *Goodison*, p. 80.

GODWIN, SIR HARRY

Born 1901. Admitted scholar, 1919; B.A. 1922; M.A., Ph.D. 1926; Sc.D. 1942. University Demonstrator and later Lecturer in Botany, 1926-48. Reader in Quaternary Research, 1948-60. Professor of Botany, 1960-68. Fellow since 1925. F.R.S. 1945. Knighted 1970. [*Who's Who*]

117 By RUPERT SHEPHARD, 1969

$17\frac{1}{4}$ x 12 in. (43.8 x 30.5 cm.). Black chalk. Head and shoulders, facing half right. Bare-headed, clean-shaven. Wears jacket; knotted tie. Signed and dated lower left, 'Rupert Shephard 1969'.

Commissioned by the College, 1969.

GUNNING, PETER

1614-1684. Matriculated sizar from Clare, 1629; B.A. 1632-3; M.A. 1636; D.D. from Corpus Christi College, 1660 (*Lit. Reg.*). Fellow of Corpus from 1633 until his ejection in 1644. B.D. Oxford, 1646. Lady Margaret Professor, 1660-1; Regius Professor of Divinity, 1661-74. Master of Corpus, 1661.

Master of St. John's, 1661–9. An ardent royalist, he had many preferments. Bishop of Chichester 1670–5, and of Ely 1675–84. [*D.N.B.*; *Venn*, I.ii, 274; *N.C.B.E.L.*, i, 1992]

118 Copy after an unknown painter of the late seventeenth century
$48\frac{1}{4} \times 38\frac{3}{8}$ in. (122.5 × 97.5 cm.). Canvas. Three-quarter length seated, turned and facing half right, looking front. Black cap over curly grey hair; grey beard and moustache. Wears episcopal rochet and chimere, with bands. Right arm on the arm of the chair, the left elbow rests on a table right, the hand holding a book. A red curtain behind the figure.

Given by the Rev. H. J. Carter, 1894.[a]

The original is in the Old Schools, Cambridge. It may probably be dated from the time when he was already Bishop of Ely, as it corresponds closely with an engraving by David Loggan (bust length, in the same direction) lettered 'Eliensis Episcopus'.[b] For the gifts of copies from the Rev. H. J. Carter, see no. **122**, note (d).

REPRODUCED. M. D. Forbes, *Clare College*, i (1928), 152, pl. XII.

NOTES. (a) Minutes of the University Library Syndicate (where the original then was), 6 June 1894, giving permission, on the application of the Master of Clare College, for the Rev. H. J. Carter to have a copy made. (b) See *Goodison*, p. 19.

HENCHMAN, HUMPHREY

1592–1675. Matriculated pensioner from Christ's, 1609; B.A. 1612–13; M.A. 1616; B.D. from Clare, 1623; D.D. 1628. Fellow, 1617. Prebendary and Precentor of Salisbury, 1623–60, and holder of other preferments of which he was deprived in the Civil War. Aided Charles II after the battle of Worcester. Bishop of Salisbury 1660–3, and of London 1663–75. Benefactor. [*D.N.B.*; *Venn*, I.ii, 353]

119 By ROBERT FARREN after (?) SIR PETER LELY
$48\frac{1}{2} \times 39$ in. (123.2 × 99.1 cm.). Canvas. To knees seated, turned and facing half left, looking front. Wears square black cap over long grey hair; grey beard and moustache. Episcopal rochet and chimere, turned-over white collar. To left books on a red-covered table, a dark curtain draped above; left hand rests on the arm of the chair holding gloves.

Commissioned 1891.

This is a copy by Farren, made in 1891 to the order of the College, from a portrait of Henchman injured 'in the recent fire'.[a] The original was already in the College by about 1790,[b] and was a version of a portrait by Lely now belonging to the Earl of Clarendon, which probably formed part of the collection of portraits made by the first Earl at Clarendon House from about 1667. The Lely is of about 1670.[c] A small water-colour copy by Silvester Harding (1745–1809) of the Clare College original is included in an extra-illustrated copy of Clarendon's *History of the rebellion*, iv, 191-272, in the Sutherland Collection, Ashmolean Museum, Oxford.

NOTES. (a) College Order Book, 21 May 1891, minute 3, and College Audit Book, Michaelmas 1890-91; the fire took place on 28 October 1890. (b) *Masters*, p. 24, no. 6. (c) R. B. Beckett, *Lely* (1851), p. 48.

HORT, JOSIAH

*c.*1674-1751. Educated at a dissenting academy but in due course conformed and admitted sizar 1704. Ordained priest, 1705. Chaplain to the Lord-Lieutenant of Ireland. Dean of Cloyne 1718-20, and of Ardagh 1720-2; Bishop of Ferns and Leighlin 1722-7, and of Kilmore and Ardagh 1727-41. Archbishop of Tuam 1742-51. A lifelong friend of Isaac Watts. Many of his sermons published. [*D.N.B.*; *Venn*, I.ii, 411]

120 Copy after an unknown painter

$49\frac{5}{8} \times 39\frac{1}{2}$ in. (126.1 × 100.4 cm.). Canvas. To knees seated, turned half right, facing and looking quarter left. Bare-headed, light wig; clean-shaven. Wears episcopal rochet and chimere, with bands. Right hand rests on arm of chair, left rests on knee with forefinger extended. Tall red back of chair to left.

Given by the Rev. H. J. Carter, 1897.[a]

The original belongs (1963) to Lady (Gwendolene) Hort, Omagh, Northern Ireland, and was lent in 1872 to the Exhibition of Arts, Industries and Manufactures in Dublin by Sir William Hort, Bart., painter unknown. As he is shown in episcopal attire, the portrait cannot be before 1722, when he became Bishop of Ferns.

NOTE. (a) College Order Book, 29 October 1897, minute 3.

JONES, OWEN THOMAS

1878-1967. Educated at University College, Aberystwyth, where he graduated with a first class degree in physics. Admitted Trinity College, 1900; B.A. 1902; M.A. 1906. Professor of Geology at Aberystwyth 1910-19, Manchester 1919-30. and Cambridge 1930-43. Fellow of Clare 1930. D.Sc. and Hon. LL.D. (Wales). F.R.S. 1926. [*D.N.B. 1961-70; Venn*, II.iii, 606; *Biographical Memoirs of Fellows of the Royal Society*, xiii (1967), 223-43]

121 By FRANK FREEMAN, 1954

$16\frac{1}{4} \times 13\frac{1}{8}$ in. (41.2 × 33.3 cm.). Water-colour and body-colour on paper. Head and shoulders, half left. Bare-headed; moustache. Signed and dated lower right, 'Freeman 1954'.

Commissioned by the College.[a]

NOTE. (a) Presumably in 1954, but this has not proved to be verifiable.

LATIMER, HUGH

*c.*1485–1555. Perhaps educated at Peterhouse. B.A. 1510–11; M.A. 1514; B.D. 1524. Fellow 1510, but not in 1536. Ordained 1515. University chaplain and cross-keeper 1522–9. University Preacher 1523. Chaplain to Anne Boleyn. Bishop of Worcester from 1535 to 1539 when he resigned owing to trouble with the king. He declined reinstatement under Edward, and was condemned for heresy and burnt at Oxford under Mary. A celebrated preacher and prose writer. [*D.N.B.*; *Venn*, I.iii, 49; *N.C.B.E.L.*, i, 1812–13]

122 Painter unknown, after an original probably of the late sixteenth century $44\frac{1}{2} \times 32\frac{1}{2}$ in. (113.0 × 85.1 cm.). Canvas. Long half-length standing, turned and facing quarter left, looking front. Black cap; grey beard and moustache. Wears episcopal rochet and chimere, a book in its chemise wrapper at his girdle. With his left hand he grasps a staff, his right is held across the body. Inscribed along the top, 'HVGO LATIMER EPS QVONDA WIGORNIENSIS PRO VERITATE EVANGELICA IGNI TRADITVS FVIT OXONIAE 16 OCTOBRIS A[o] DNI 1555 AETATIS SVAE 74.'[a] Inscribed to right of head, 'NIHIL EST OPERTV QVOD NON REVELABITVR MAT 10.'[b] Upper left is his coat of arms.[c]

(?) Given by the Rev. H. J. Carter, before 1897.[d]

Copy of a portrait on wood in the Deanery, Canterbury, which is probably of the late sixteenth century.

NOTES. (a) This is the inscription on the original, transcribed on the copy with several mistakes. 'Hugh Latimer, formerly Bishop of Worcester, for truth of doctrine was consigned to the flames at Oxford on 16 October 1555, aged seventy-four.' (b) 'There is nothing covered that shall not be revealed,' Matthew x. 26. (c) Gules, a cross patonce or, over all a bend azure semée-de-lis of the second, though the bend is here sable. (d) *Atkinson and Clark*, p. 310, list it, on the authority of the then Master, Dr. E. Atkinson, among a number of 'recent copies, lately presented to the College', some of which have been identified from College records as the gifts of the Rev. H. J. Carter, made between 1892 and 1899.

LOVE, RICHARD

1596–1661. Born in Cambridge, son of an apothecary. Matriculated pensioner from King's College 1611; B.A. from Clare 1614–5; M.A. 1618; D.D. 1630. Fellow 1618–30. Taxor 1625–6. Senior Proctor 1628–9. Master of Corpus Christi College 1632–61. Vice-Chancellor 1633–4. Lady Margaret Professor 1649. Chaplain to the King. Rector of Eckington (Derbys.) 1629–61. Prebendary of Lichfield 1631–61. Dean of Ely 1660. Buried in the Chapel. Benefactor. [*D.N.B.*; *Venn*, I.iii, 107]

123 Painter unknown, after an original attributed to DANIEL MYTENS $30 \times 24\frac{1}{2}$ in. (76.2 × 62.2 cm.). Canvas. Half-length, slightly to right, right hand on breast. Black cap; grey beard and moustache. Wears black academical gown over black dress with white cuffs, white collar with tassel. In background to right, a landscape.

Source of acquisition unknown.

The original of which this is a copy, is at Corpus Christi College, to which it was given by Thomas Tenison, Archbishop of Canterbury, Love's son-in-law. It has been attributed to Daniel Mytens, but unconvincingly, though it bears a general resemblance to his style. This copy, made in 1962, replaces another given to Clare College by the Rev. H. J. Carter in 1898, subsequently burnt.

MOLLISON, WILLIAM LOUDON

1851–1929. Educated at Aberdeen; M.A. there 1872, Hon. LL.D. 1897. Admitted scholar 1872; B.A. (second Wrangler and second Smith's Prizeman) 1876; M.A. 1879; LL.D. 1916. Fellow, 1876; Tutor, 1880–1913; Master, 1915–29. Secretary of the General Board of Studies, 1904–15. Mathematician and classical scholar noted for 'energy and perseverance'. Benefactor. [*Venn*, II.iv, 435]

124 By HENRY LAMB, R.A.   PLATE X

$26\frac{5}{8} \times 21\frac{1}{2}$ in. (67.6 × 54.6 cm.). Canvas. Short half-length, to right, head inclined to his right. Bare-headed, receding hair, grey moustache and chin beard. Wears dark clothes, with black academical gown. Patterned background. Signed upper right, 'Lamb'.

Commissioned by the College, (?) 1926 (see REPRODUCED below).

This portrait of him was not liked by Dr. Mollison, which presumably led to the later painting by Hugh Buss (below).

REPRODUCED. *Clare Association Annual 1926*, frontispiece.

125 By HUGH BUSS, 1930

$26\frac{1}{2} \times 21\frac{1}{2}$ in. (67.3 × 54.6 cm.). Canvas. Nearly half-length, quarter right, slightly bent posture, right hand held across in front. White moustache and beard. Wears black velvet doctor's cap, with scarlet gown of Doctor of Laws, over dark clothes. Signed upper right, 'HB', in a monogram.

Commissioned by the College, 1930.

Inscribed at the back, 'Painted by Hugh Buss (M.A. and formerly classical scholar of Clare) 1930, mainly from a photograph of Dr. Mollison in cap and gown (black) taken by Messrs. Palmer Clarke'.[a]

NOTE. (a) The photograph is reproduced in M. D. Forbes, *Clare College*, ii (1930), 632, pl. XXX.

MOORE, JOHN

1646–1714. Admitted sizar, 1662; B.A. 1665–6; M.A. 1669; D.D. 1681. Fellow, 1667–77. Ordained 1671. Held several appointments and preferments including that of Chaplain to William and Mary. Bishop of Norwich 1691–1707, and of Ely 1707–14. Buried in Ely Cathedral. Took much interest in medicine and book collecting. His large and valuable library was purchased by George I and presented to the University. Benefactor to the College library. [*D.N.B.; Venn*, I.iii, 206]

126 By SIR GODFREY KNELLER, 1705   PLATE VII

49 × 39½ in. (124.5 × 100.3 cm.). Canvas. To below knees seated, turned and facing half right, looking front. Bare-headed, own long iron-grey hair; clean-shaven; dark, warm complexion. Wears episcopal rochet and chimere, with black scarf and bands. Right hand on arm of chair, left hand in front of body. On table right a black academical cap. Signed and dated lower left, 'G. Kneller pt/1705'.

Source of acquisition unknown. *Masters*, p. 23, no. 4, records one portrait, and another came in 1797/98;[a] but nothing is known to distinguish either of these portraits from the other (see no. **127** below).

A painting of fine quality, when he was Bishop of Norwich. A copy by Isaac Whood, dated 1736, is in the University Library, Cambridge,[b], and another copy, of poor quality, is in the Bishop's House at Ely. A mezzotint by W. Faithorne jun.,[c] which closely follows the Clare portrait in reverse, with the addition of a pilaster behind the table, perhaps indicates another, unknown, version. Francis Blomefield remarks of the mezzotint that it is 'said to be of a great likeness'.[d] On Moore's first visitation of Cambridge as Bishop of Ely, in 1708, Clare College presented him with an address referring to his great gifts to the College library and towards the new buildings.

REPRODUCED. *Connoisseur*, cxl (1957), 233.

NOTES. (a) College Audit Book, Michaelmas 1797–Michaelmas 1798, 'Carriage of B[p]. Moore's Picture 7 6'. (b) *Goodison*, p. 39. (c) J. Chaloner Smith, *British mezzotinto portraits*, Part II (1879), p. 469, no. 25. (d) Francis Blomefield, *An essay towards a topographical history of the county of Norfolk*, ii (1739), 423.

127 Painter unknown

49½ × 39⅜ in. (125.7 × 100.0 cm.). Canvas. To knees seated, turned and facing half right, looking front. Bare-headed, own long grey hair; clean-shaven. Wears episcopal rochet and chimere, with bands. Right hand on arm of chair, left turns pages of a book on a table right. Background shelves of books, covered by a curtain behind the figure.

Source of acquisition unknown. See above no. **126**.

This has considerable similarities to no. **126** above, both conforming basic-ally to the same portrait-pattern; as he wears bishop's robes, it cannot be before 1691, when he became Bishop of Norwich. The two variants have been much confused, a confusion which apparently goes back to the Rev. Cecil Moore's enumeration of the Bishop's portraits in 1884.[a] No. **126** above was not then identified as the work of Kneller, and it seems to be this latter por-trait which he suggests '*may* be the work of Kersseboom, who painted several of the Bishop's children'. A version is at Lambeth Palace, wrongly ascribed to Kneller, with whom it has no connection. It is perhaps just worth remem-bering the Rev. Cecil Moore's guess about Johann Kerseboom (active 1680, d.1708) in considering the possible authorship of this portrait-pattern.

REPRODUCED. M. D. Forbes, *Clare College*, i (1928), pl. V.

NOTE. (a) *The Bibliographer*, vi (1884), 93, reprinted as *Memoir of the Rt. Rev. John Moore, D.D., Lord Bishop of Ely* (1885), p. 36.

NEWCASTLE, THOMAS PELHAM-HOLLES, first Duke of

1693-1768. Admitted Fellow-Commoner, 1709-10; LL.D. 1728. Sometime Lord Lieutenant of Middlesex and of Nottinghamshire. Created Earl of Clare 1714, and Duke of Newcastle 1715. Held high office in Whig administrations, and was a master of political patronage. High Steward of the University, 1737; Chancellor, 1748-68. [*D.N.B.*; *Venn*, I.iii, 336; see also D. A. Winstanley, *The University of Cambridge in the Eighteenth Century* (1922), and biographies by R. A. Kelch (1974), and R. Browning (1975).]

128 Attributed to WILLIAM HOARE

$93\frac{1}{4} \times 56$ in. (236.8 × 142.2 cm.). Canvas. Whole-length standing, turned front, facing quarter right, looking front. Bare-headed, white periwig; clean-shaven. Wears Garter robes. Left hand on hip, right holding a paper. To left a gilt table with his plumed hat; in background right a column, a red curtain looped across at the top.

Source of acquisition unknown. *Masters* p. 24, no. 8.

In appearance he seems to be aged about fifty. Another version belonged about 1927 to Lord Cranworth.[a]

REPRODUCED. D. A. Winstanley, *op. cit.*, frontispiece.

NOTE. (a) F. Duleep Singh, ed. Rev. E. Farrer, *Portraits in Norfolk Houses*, (c.1927), i, 397, no. 51, the description of which corresponds in its essentials exactly with this picture, but it is unattributed.

SASSOON, SIEGFRIED LORAINE

1886-1967. Admitted 1905; no degree. Country gentleman and publisher of verse. Commissioned in the Royal Welch Fusiliers, 1915, and had a distinguished war record. M.C. His experiences produced anti-war poetry that brought both fame and notoriety. Literary editor of the *Daily Herald*, 1919. Hawthornden and James Tait Black prizes for *Memoirs of a Fox-hunting Man*, 1928. Hon. D.Litt. (Liverpool) 1931; C.B.E. 1951; Queen's Medal for Poetry, 1957; Hon. D.Litt. (Oxford) 1965. Elected Hon. Fellow of the College, 1953. [*D.N.B. 1961-70; N.C.B.E.L.*, iv, 337-40]

129 By SIR WILLIAM ROTHENSTEIN

$9 \times 7\frac{1}{2}$ in. (22.8 × 19.1 cm.). Black chalk. Head, facing and looking half left, Bare-headed, clean-shaven.

Source of acquisition unknown.[a]

Very similar to another drawing of Sassoon by Rothenstein, signed, and dated 1921.[b]

NOTES. (a) The label on the frame includes the date 1921, but this seems likely to refer to the date of the drawing. (b) Reproduced in *Twenty-four portraits by William Rothenstein, second series* (1923).

TERRICK, RICHARD

1710–1777. Admitted pensioner, 1726; B.A. 1729–30; M.A. 1733; D.D. 1747. Fellow, 1731–8. Ordained priest, 1734. Preacher at the Rolls Chapel, 1736–57; Canon of Windsor, 1742–9; Chaplain to the King, 1745–57; Canon of St. Paul's, 1749–57; Bishop of Peterborough 1757–64, and of London 1764–77. Benefactor to the College Chapel, which he consecrated in 1769. [*D.N.B.*; *Venn*, I.iv, 215]

130 Copy by JOSEPH FREEMAN after N. DANCE, R.A. (Sir Nathaniel Dance-Holland, Bt.)

$49\frac{1}{2} \times 39\frac{1}{2}$ in. (125.7 × 100.3 cm.). Canvas. To below knees seated, turned and facing half left, looking front, the right arm resting on a table, a book held on his knee in the left hand, the first finger between the leaves. Bare-headed, cauliflower wig; clean-shaven. Wears episcopal rochet and chimere, with black scarf and bands. To left books on a table, a brown curtain falling across them from above. Inscribed lower right, '1771/Freeman Pinxt/from N. Dance'.[a]

Source of acquisition unknown. *Masters*, p. 23, no. 5.

The original by Dance is only known from a mezzotint of 1770 by E. Fisher.[b] Another copy, which has wrongly been claimed as the original,[c] belongs to Sion College, London, and a third, head and shoulders only, is at Fulham Palace, London.

NOTES. (a) Presumably the Joseph Freeman, who in 1776 was employed by the University for cleaning pictures and repairing frames in the University Library, see *Goodison*, p. 3, note (a) to Colet. (b) J. Chaloner Smith, *British mezzotinto portraits*, Part II (1879), p. 506, no. 57. (c) By the *Dictionary of National Biography*. Terrick gave this portrait to Sion College in 1771 (see E. H. Pearce, *Sion College and library* (1913), p. 28), but its quality proclaims it a copy and not an original.

THIRKILL, SIR HENRY

1886–1971. Admitted scholar, 1905; B.A. 1908; M.A. 1912. Fellow, 1910–39, 1958–71; Tutor, 1920–39; President, 1930–39; Master, 1939–58. Vice-Chancellor, 1945–7. Served in East Africa in the Great War. M.C. 1918. Assistant Demonstrator in Experimental Physics, 1912–19; Demonstrator, 1919–26; Lecturer, 1926–33. C.B.E. 1946; knighted 1951. [*Who's Who*; *Clare Association Annual 1971*, pp. 8–18]

131 By W. G. de GLEHN, R.A., 1947

$49 \times 39\frac{1}{2}$ in. (124.5 × 100.3 cm.). Canvas. To knees, seated half to right; right hand on knee, left forearm on arm of chair. Bare-headed, dark hair; clean-shaven. Wears black academical gown over grey suit. To left, books on a table. Signed upper right, 'W G de Glehn'.

Commissioned by the College, 1947.

Painted 'last summer, shortly before the Master ceased to be Vice-Chancellor',[a] that is, presumably, in 1947. This portrait of him was not liked by Sir Henry Thirkill.

REPRODUCED. *Clare Association Annual 1948*, frontispiece.

NOTE. (a) *Clare Association Annual 1948*, p. 4.

132   By FRANK EASTMAN, 1953   PLATE XII

$39\frac{3}{8} \times 29\frac{3}{8}$ in. (100.0 × 74.6 cm.). Canvas. Three-quarter length, seated, half to right; left hand holds book on knee, right hand on arm of chair. Bare-headed, clean-shaven; receding dark hair. Bookcases in background. Signed and dated lower left, 'Frank Eastman 1953'.

Commissioned by Sir Henry Thirkill, who gave it to the College at a date unknown. *At present (1985) on loan to the Leys School, Cambridge.*

The portrait is a good likeness. Thirkill asked that the College should hang this portrait in preference to the one by de Glehn.

THIRKILL, SIR HENRY, with HARRISON, WILLIAM JOHN and TELFER, WILLIAM

Thirkill: see above for biography

William John Harrison: 1884–1969. Admitted scholar, 1903; B.A. 1906; M.A. 1910. Fellow 1907, re-elected 1913. Lecturer in Mathematics, University of Liverpool, 1910–14. M.B.E. for war work. University Lecturer in Mathematics, 1919–31. Bursar, 1926–49. [*Clare Association Annual 1969*, pp. 56–7, and *1971*, pp. 22–3]

William Telfer: 1886–1968. Admitted scholar, 1905; B.A. 1908; M.A. 1916; B.D. 1932; D.D. 1937. Ordained priest, 1910, and served in the Clare Mission in Rotherhithe. M.C. 1916. Vicar of All Saints, Rotherhithe, 1919–21. Fellow, 1921–46; Dean, Praelector, and Assistant Tutor. University Lecturer in Divinity, 1926–44 and from 1947; Ely Professor of Divinity, 1944–46. Honorary Fellow, 1947–68. Master of Selwyn College, 1947–56, and Fellow thereafter. [*Who's Who; Clare Association Annual 1968*, pp. 62–3]

133   By TERENCE TENISON CUNEO, 1949

$32\frac{1}{4} \times 42\frac{3}{4}$ in. (81.9 × 108.6 cm.). Canvas. Conversation piece. In the Combination Room, at one end of a long table, Thirkill stands at the right addressing Harrison seated at the left, opposite whom Telfer is seated. On the table are papers, books and writing materials. To left is a small round table with two silver vessels on it. Through two windows to the right a view is seen into the College court. Signed and dated lower left, 'Cuneo/November/1949'.

Commissioned by the College, 1949.

TILLOTSON, JOHN

1630–1694. Admitted pensioner, 1647; B.A. 1650; M.A. 1654; D.D. 1666. Fellow from 1651 until his deprivation in 1661. Chaplain to the King, 1666–91. F.R.S. 1671. Dean of Canterbury, 1672–89; Canon of St. Paul's, 1675–91; Archbishop of Canterbury, 1691–4. A distinguished preacher. Author, sermons. [*D.N.B.; Venn*, I.iv, 242; *N.C.B.E.L.*, ii, 1616–17]

134   Painter unknown, after SIR GODFREY KNELLER

$47\frac{5}{8} \times 40$ in. (120.9 × 101.6 cm.). Canvas. Three-quarter length seated, turned and facing half left, looking front. Bare-headed, his own grey hair; clean-shaven. Wears episcopal rochet and chimere with bands. Left hand on arm of chair, right hand on his knee.

Given by J. R. Harris, 1901.[a]

This corresponds to a Kneller at Lambeth Palace,[b] of which another version, engraved by G. Vertue, is at Eastnor Castle, a portrait-pattern which must have originated between 1681 and 1684, as it shows him in bishop's robes. A half-length copy is in the National Portrait Gallery (no. 94), and a head and shoulders was in 1934 the property of Mr. J. Tillotson. There are numerous engravings of this portrait-pattern. See also no. **135** below.

NOTES. (a) College Order Book, 31 May 1901, minute 1a, to be hung in the Hall. Another portrait of Tillotson was already in the College by that time, listed by *Atkinson and Clark*, p. 310, as in the Combination Room. As a portrait of Tillotson hung there until recently, on balance it is probable that the portrait now in the Hall should be identified as the one given by J. R. Harris, whose gift is not otherwise identifiable. (b) Rep. G. M. Bevan, *Portraits of the Archbishops of Canterbury* (1908), p. 36.

135　Painter unknown, after SIR GODFREY KNELLER

$50\frac{1}{4} \times 40$ in. (127.6 × 101.6 cm.). Canvas. To knees seated, turned and facing half left, looking front. Bare-headed, his own grey hair; clean-shaven. Wears episcopal rochet and chimere with bands. Left hand on arm of chair, right hand on a book on table left. Red curtain draped at left behind.

Source of acquisition unknown.[a] *Masters* p. 24, no. 7.

This follows the same Kneller portrait-pattern as no. **134** above, with the slight variation in the disposition of the right hand.

NOTE. (a) See note (a) to no. **134** above.

TOWNSHEND, CHARLES

1725–1767. Admitted Fellow-Commoner, 1747; M.A. 1749. Lawyer and M.P. Lord of Trade, 1749–54; Treasurer of the Chamber, 1756–61; Secretary at War, 1761–2; Paymaster, 1765–6; Chancellor of the Exchequer, 1766–7. Suspended the New York Assembly and established Commissioners of Customs to raise money in America. A brilliant orator whose political career was 'spoilt by instability and lack of principle'. [*D.N.B.*; *Venn*, I.iv, 258]

136　By ROBERT FARREN, after SIR JOSHUA REYNOLDS, P.R.A.

$93\frac{1}{2} \times 58$ in. (237.5 × 147.3 cm.). Canvas. Whole-length standing, turned three-quarters left, facing half left, looking front. Bare-headed, grey wig; clean-shaven. Over red velvet clothes wears the gold-laced black gown of the Chancellor of the Exchequer. Right hand rests on papers on table left, left holds a paper. Background right a large urn on a pedestal, a patterned red curtain falling from above it to the left.

Given by the Rev. H. J. Carter, 1896.[a]

Copied from the original at Raynham Hall, Norfolk, 1896, for the Rev. H. J. Carter.[b] Reynolds's portrait may be dated to 1767; [c] it was sold from

Raynham Hall in 1904, and bought back again by the Marquess Townshend in 1950.

NOTES. (a) College Order Book, 30 October 1896, minute 4. (b) From a manuscript label at the back of the picture. (c) From Reynolds's ledgers, see *Walpole Society*, xlii (1970), 137. Cf. E. K. Waterhouse, *Reynolds* (1941), p. 55.

WARDALE, JOHN REYNOLDS

1859–1931. Admitted 1878, B.A. (second classic) 1882; M.A. 1885. Fellow 1882–1931, tutor 1894–1920. Professor of Latin at University College, Cardiff, 1883–8. President of the Cambridge Philological Society, 1918–19. Edited *Clare College Letters and Documents*. [*Venn*, II.vi, 349]

137 By F. M. BENNETT, 1912

$19\frac{1}{4} \times 15\frac{1}{2}$ in. (48.9 × 38.7 cm.). Canvas. Bust, turned half right. Bare-headed, thin grey hair, grey moustache. Spectacles. Wears dark suit; white butterfly collar. Signed and dated upper left, 'F. M. Bennett 1912'.

Source of acquisition unknown.

WEBB, WILLIAM

1775–1856. Admitted pensioner, 1793; later scholar; B.A. 1797; M.A. 1800; B.D. 1808; D.D.1816. Fellow 1799. Tutor. Master 1815–56. Vice-Chancellor 1817–18 and 1832–3. Ordained priest, 1801. Vicar of Litlington (Cambs.), 1816–56, where he died. [*Venn*, II.vi, 388]

138 Painter unknown

$33\frac{1}{4} \times 27\frac{1}{4}$ in. (84.5 × 69.2 cm.). Canvas. Half-length seated, turned and facing half left, looking front. Bare-headed, dark receding hair; clean-shaven. Wears black academical gown over dark dress, with choker and bands. Left hand rests on thigh, right on a book resting on edge on table left.

Source of acquisition unknown.[a]

NOTE. (a) As it is not listed in *Atkinson and Clark* in 1897, it presumably came after this date; his son Theodore Vincent Webb died in 1885, but it is not mentioned in the will of his widow, Martha Sophia Webb, who died in 1909.

WHISTON, WILLIAM

1667–1752. Admitted sizar, 1686; B.A. 1689–90; M.A. 1693. Fellow, 1691. Ordained deacon, 1693. Chaplain to Bishop Moore of Norwich. Lucasian Professor in succession to Newton, 1702–10. Expelled from the University for Arianism and travelled the country expounding eccentric scientific and theological views especially about the fulfilment of biblical prophecies. His translation of the works of Josephus (1737) was standard for a century and a half. [*D.N.B.*; *Venn*, I.iv, 384; *N.C.B.E.L.*, ii, 1871]

139 Painter unknown, after SARAH HOADLY

$20\frac{1}{2} \times 15\frac{1}{2}$ in. (52.1 × 39.4 cm.). Canvas. Bust, turned and facing half right, looking front, head bent forward. Bare-headed, longish grey hair; clean-shaven.

Wears dark dress, white neckerchief and bands. Inscribed upper left, 'Willm. Whiston/A.M.'.

Source of acquisition unknown.^{a}

Probably copied from the portrait in the National Portrait Gallery (no. 243), which is considered to be itself a copy after Sarah Hoadly's original, engraved by G. Vertue in 1720. The engraving shows him at half-length, holding an open book in his left hand. The original is likely to be the portrait 'in the family collection at Lyndon Hall, the house of his son-in-law, Thomas Barker, where Whiston died'.^{b}

REPRODUCED. M. D. Forbes, *Clare College*, i (1928), 152, pl. XII.

NOTES. (a) Not listed by *Atkinson and Clark* in 1897, but like a number of other portraits in the College which are copies, perhaps given by the Rev. H. J. Carter, whose latest recorded gift was made in 1899, see no. 114, note (b). (b) David Piper, *Catalogue of seventeenth-century portraits in the National Portrait Gallery* (1963), p. 374.

WILSON, GODFREY HAROLD ALFRED

1871–1958. Admitted scholar, 1892; B.A. 1895; M.A. 1899. Fellow, 1897–1929, 1939–58; Bursar, 1913; Master, 1929–39; M.P. for the University, 1929–35; Vice-Chancellor, 1935–7. Secretary of the Financial Board, 1920–6, and Treasurer of the University, 1926–9. O.B.E. 1919. Hon. D.C.L. (Durham), 1937. [*Venn*, II.vi, 520; *Who's Who; Clare Association Annual 1958*, pp.9–13]

140 By THOMAS GUNN   PLATE X

$29\frac{1}{2} \times 24\frac{5}{8}$ in. (74.9 × 62.5 cm.). Canvas. Half-length seated, front, hands clasped in his lap, leaning to his left. Bare-headed, grey hair; grey moustache. Over black cassock wears Vice-Chancellor's scarlet cope with a white fur cape; wing collar and black bow tie, with bands. Signed upper left, 'Thomas Gunn'.

Commissioned by the College, (?) 1936–37.

As the portrait is reproduced in the *Clare Association Annual* for 1937, it was presumably painted during Wilson's second term of office as Vice-Chancellor in 1936–37.

REPRODUCED. *Clare Association Annual 1937*, p. 5.

WOODROOFE (or WOODROFFE), THOMAS

1750–1817. Admitted sizar, 1765; later scholar; B.A. 1770; M.A. 1773; B.D. 1783. Fellow, 1770. Ordained priest, 1774. Rector of Ockley (Surrey), 1784–1817, and of Oving (Sussex), 1799–1814. Twice married. [*Venn*, II.vi, 572]

141 Painter unknown, 1773

$29\frac{1}{4} \times 24\frac{3}{4}$ in. (74.3 × 61.9 cm.). Canvas. Nearly half-length, half to right. Bare-headed, clean-shaven; the unpowdered hair taken back, with a roll curl over each ear. Black academical gown, with bands, over grey dress. Inscribed upper right, '1773/Ætatis/24'.

Bought by the College, 1934.

In 1773 Woodroofe took his degree of Master of Arts, and was ordained deacon. Another portrait of him is, or was, at Hackford Hall, Norfolk, in the possession of the Collyer family, together with one of the Rev. Daniel Collyer, who is described as a college friend of Woodroofe.[a] They seem to be companion portraits, and have been dated c.1770,[b] the year in which Woodroofe became a Fellow of Clare. Collyer migrated from Trinity Hall to Clare in 1773, and became a Fellow in 1774.

NOTES. (a) Prince Frederick Duleep Singh, ed. Rev. Edmund Farrer, *Portraits in Norfolk houses*, 2 vols., n.d., I. pp. 203, no. 13, 206, no. 31; list dated 1908. (b) *Idem.*

UNKNOWN NOBLEMAN, early seventeenth century

142 Painter unknown
$76\frac{1}{4} \times 47\frac{1}{4}$ in. (193.7 × 120.0 cm.). Canvas. Whole-length standing, turned and facing slightly right, looking front. Black hat with jewel at (his) right side; light coloured moustache and chin beard. Wears a scarlet baron's mantle with two bands of white fur, collar and Greater George of the Garter, wide pleated ruff. His gloved right hand placed upon his hip; leans on his left elbow, the bare hand holding a glove. At the top a draped curtain across each corner.

Purchased, perhaps 1939. Coll. Margaret, Dowager Lady Willoughby de Broke (d.1880), bought about 1854;[a] her niece, Miss Mary Williams, by 1923;[b] anon. sale (= Miss Mary Williams), Christie's, 14 March 1924 (57), bt. Pawsey & Payne; Captain N. R. Colville, M.C., Penheale Manor, Cornwall; Colville sale, Christie's, 24 February 1939 (114), bt. Dulan.

Formerly called Thomas Cecil, 2nd Baron Burghley and 1st Earl of Exeter (1542-1623). If it were he, the date would have to be between 1601, when he received the Garter, and 1605, when he was created Earl of Exeter. But as he wears the robes of a baron, and a ruff of about 1615, the identification of the portrait as of Exeter must be excluded.[c] For an authentic portrait of him, see no. **113**.

REPRODUCED. *Connoisseur*, lxvi (1923), 227; H. K. Morse, *Elizabethan pageantry* (1934), p. 89.

NOTES. (a) *Connoisseur*, lxvi (1923), 227, note by Miss Mary Williams, niece of the Dowager Lady Willoughby de Broke. (b) See note (a). (c) Roy Strong, *Tudor and Jacobean portraits* (National Portrait Gallery, 1969), i, 118.

SIDNEY SUSSEX COLLEGE

The usual dearth of information on the acquisition of College portraits, before fairly recent times, is to some extent compensated in the case of Sidney Sussex College by the series of inventories, beginning in 1639, drawn up at the entry into office of each Master of the College, in whose Lodge, until late in the nineteenth century, the great majority of the portraits hung. To have these limiting dates for the entry of a portrait into the possession of the College is of interest in itself, and on occasion can permit of useful inferences being drawn. The whole-length portrait of the Foundress, the most important as well as the finest in the College (no. **181**), attributed to Steven van der Meulen, may be dated from the costume to about 1565, during her lifetime. As it appears in the 1639 inventory it is a likely inference that it came through her executors, when the College was founded under the terms of her will in 1596. Though Dr. Gabriel Goodman bequeathed a portrait of her in 1601, the balance of probability strongly favours this being identifiable with no. **182**, perhaps by George Gower, also in the 1639 inventory, rather than with the stately whole-length. This inventory also records a portrait of the first Master of the College, James Montagu, Bishop of Winchester, (no. **171**), and the next one, of 1688, a portrait of another early Master, Samuel Ward (no. **189**), under whom the inventory of 1639 was drawn up. From then onwards until relatively recent times the existence of portraits of only five more Masters is known from the inventories and from other sources. The modern practice of commissioning portraits has provided an unbroken sequence from that of George Arthur Weekes (nos. **190-1**) until today.

The most famous alumnus of the College, Oliver Cromwell, is represented by three portraits (nos. **153-5**). The larger oil painting is a good example of a much repeated standard likeness. The smaller one and the pastel are both related to the portraits of him by the famous miniaturist Samuel Cooper, but the traditional attribution of the pastel to Cooper's own hand must now, in the light of modern criticism, be reluctantly abandoned.

Exceptionally, the Chapel altarpiece by Pittoni is included after the catalogue of portraits, on account of its artistic and art-historical interest.

AGAR, JOHN NEWTON

Born 1914. Admitted scholar 1932; B.A. 1935; M.A. 1939; Ph.D. 1938. Fellow 1950. University Demonstrator in Physical Chemistry 1947; University Lecturer 1948; University Reader in Physical Chemistry 1965–81.

143 By MICHAEL NOAKES, 1981–82

$22 \times 15\frac{1}{2}$ in. (55.9 × 59.4 cm.). Pencil on white paper. Half-length, seated to left; in raised right hand holds a pipe, left hand on leg. Bare-headed, clean-shaven, spectacles. Wears jacket with collar and tie. Signed lower right, 'Michael Noakes/1981–82'.

Commissioned by his former students, 1981.

A good likeness.

BLUNDELL, PETER, *Called*

1520–1601. Clothier, of Tiverton (Devon). Founder of Blundell's School and a principal benefactor of the College. [*D.N.B.*]

144 Copy after an original by an unknown painter

$28\frac{1}{4} \times 23\frac{1}{8}$ in. (71.4 × 58.7.). Canvas, oval. Half-length, turned half right. Clean-shaven, bushy, dark hair falling in front of the shoulders. He wears black dress with a white collar-band with a deep lace edging. Behind the figure a tree-trunk, with a landscape to the right.

Given by Old Blundellians, 1889.

This is a copy of a portrait at Blundell's School, Tiverton. The original was given to the school as a portrait of Blundell by Robert Newton Incledon in 1808,[a] having been given to him by Thomas Whitmore of Apsley Park, Shropshire.[b] The Whitmore family had had a close association with Peter Blundell, and in 1694 a Sir William Whitmore presented a portrait of him to the school, which was lost in transit,[c] and seems to have disappeared. On account of the date of the costume, in the 1660s, the portrait at Blundell's School is impossible as depicting their founder. It has been suggested that it may possibly represent a later member of the Blundell family, or indeed a Whitmore;[d] such confusions of identification are not very unusual in family collections of portraits.

NOTES. (a) Arthur Fisher, in *Devon notes and queries*, iii (1904–5), 33–5, 65–8. (b) Inscription on an engraving by E. Smith, made between 1810 and 1813 (Fisher, *op. cit.*, p. 65). (c) Fisher, *op. cit.*, p. 34, quoting Benjamin Incledon's *Donations of Peter Blundell and other benefactors to the Free Grammar School at Tiverton* (1792). (d) Fisher, *op. cit.*, p. 67.

BRAMHALL, JOHN

1594–1663. Admitted scholar 1609; B.A. 1613; M.A. 1616; B.D. 1623; D.D. 1630. Chaplain to Sir Thomas Wentworth, Lord Deputy of Ireland, 1633; Treasurer of Dublin and Archdeacon of Meath 1633; Bishop of Derry 1634. In exile with other royalists on the continent, 1644–60. Archbishop of

Armagh and Primate of Ireland 1661–3. Speaker of the Irish House of Lords. Author of theological works; a stout defender of the monarchy and of the established church. [*D.N.B.*; *Venn*, I.i, 204; W. J. Sparrow-Simpson, *Archbishop Bramhall* (1927)]

145 Painter unknown

$29\frac{1}{4}$ × 24 in. (74.3 × 60.9 cm.). Canvas. Half-length, slightly right, in a painted oval. Wears black skull cap; episcopal rochet and chimere. Inscribed at right above the shoulder, 'John Bramhall DD/Primate of Ireland/1660'.

Source of acquisition unknown. First recorded in the Master's inventory (William Elliston) of 1760.

Copy after the original in the possession of the Archbishop of Armagh, at Church House, Armagh, Northern Ireland.

BUTLER, GEORGE

1774–1853. Admitted pensioner 1790; later scholar; B.A. (Senior Wrangler) 1794; M.A. 1797; B.D. 1804; D.D. (*Lit.Reg.*) 1805. Fellow 1794; Tutor and Mathematical Lecturer. Head Master of Harrow School 1805–29. Dean of Peterborough 1842–53. Mathematician and classical scholar. [*D.N.B.*; *Venn*, II.i, 476]

146 By W. E. MILLER after JACOBS[a]

$20\frac{1}{2}$ × $16\frac{1}{2}$ in. (52.1 × 41.9 cm.). Canvas. Bust, half right. Short, grey hair. Wears dark clerical dress with stock.

Given by the Rev. Dr. H. Montagu Butler, his son, Master of Trinity College, Cambridge, 1894.

The gift of the portrait marked the one hundredth anniversary of George Butler being declared Senior Wrangler. Another version of it is at Harrow School, given by the Rev. Dr. H. Montagu Butler in 1905, the hundredth anniversary of George Butler's becoming Head Master of the school; no painter's name is attached to it. The 'Jacobs' of the present portrait is possibly Joseph Jacobs, who is known as the exhibitor of a 'Portrait of a Gentleman' at the Society of British Artists in London in 1828, no. 653.

NOTE. (a) From the label on the picture.

CHAFY, WILLIAM

1779–1843. Admitted sizar at Corpus Christi College, 1796 and migrated to Sidney in that year; scholar of Sidney 1798; B.A. 1800; M.A. 1803; B.D. 1810; D.D. (*Lit.Reg.*) 1814. Fellow 1801; Tutor; Master of the College 1813–43. Vice-Chancellor 1813 and 1829. Chaplain-in-Ordinary to George III, George IV, William IV and Queen Victoria. Benefactor. [*D.N.B.*; *Venn*, II.i, 549]

147 Painter unknown

$29\frac{1}{2}$ × $24\frac{1}{2}$ in. (74.9 × 62.2 cm.). Canvas. Half-length, turned half right. Grey hair, with dark side-whiskers. Wears black academical gown over black cassock, with white stock and bands.

Source of acquisition unknown. First recorded in the Master's inventory (William Chafy) of 1813.

As he wears a black gown, probably before 1813 when he took the degree of D.D., despite the grey hair, presumably powdered.

148 Painter unknown
$35\frac{1}{2} \times 27\frac{1}{4}$ in. (90.2 × 69.2 cm.). Canvas. Half-length seated, turned half right. Wears scarlet D.D. gown with a black scarf over black cassock, with white choker and bands. Ruddy complexion. Holds an academical cap in his lap with the left hand.

Lent by Miss Esmé Chafy, his great-great-granddaughter, 1962.

Perhaps painted in or soon after 1813, when he became Master, took the degree of D.D. and became Vice-Chancellor of the University.

CHAFY, MARY M.

1778–1831. Daughter and co-heiress of William Westwood of Chatteris; married William Chafy (nos. **147-8**) in 1813.

149 Painter unknown
$35\frac{1}{2} \times 27\frac{1}{4}$ in. (90.2 × 69.2 cm.). Canvas. To knees seated, turned half left. Dark brown hair, a pink rose in front, a white veil hanging at the back of the head. Wears very pale pink, décolleté dress; bare arms. To right a draped red curtain, a garden with trees in the background.

Lent by Miss Esmé Chafy, her great-great-granddaughter, 1962.

Probably companion portrait to that of her husband, Dr. William Chafy (no. **148** above), to which it corresponds in size, and pairs off by the figure being turned in the opposite direction. Thus of about the same date, 1813, or soon after, and very likely by the same hand.

CHAFY, WILLIAM WESTWOOD

1814–1873. Only son of Dr. William and Mary Chafy (above). Admitted Fellow-Commoner 1832, but took no degree. Of Conington Hall (Cambs.); a notable rider to hounds. [*Venn*, II.i, 549]

150 Painter unknown
35 × 27 in. (88.9 × 68.6 cm.). Canvas. Whole-length standing, slightly to right. Wears pink hunting coat, with a blue waistcoat, buff breeches, and riding boots, holding a crop in his right hand. Behind and to the right brown panelling, with a window to the left, a brown table below it.

Lent by Miss Esmé Chafy, his great-granddaughter, 1963.

He married Annette Kyle; the eldest of their four children was born in 1840. See no. **151** below.

CHAFY, MRS. WILLIAM WESTWOOD, with two children

Daughter of the Rt. Rev. Samuel Kyle, Bishop of Cork, Cloyne and Ross; first wife of William Westwood Chafy (no. **150**).

151 Painter unknown

$49\frac{3}{8} \times 39\frac{3}{8}$ in. (125.4 × 97.5 cm.). Canvas. She is seated at the right on a small buff-coloured settee, wearing a blue décolleté dress; her arms are round a small boy in a red frock, seated in front of her, behind whom is a little girl in white with a blue sash. To right a red curtain, to left a landscape.

Lent by Miss Esmé Chafy, her great-granddaughter, 1963.

She was Annette Kyle. Of her four children it must be the two eldest who are shown in the picture, Mary Anne Elizabeth, born 1840, and William Kyle Westwood, born 1841. The remaining two were daughters. From the apparent ages of the two children, the date of the painting could be about 1844.

COLSON, JOHN

1680-1760. Matriculated at Christ Church, Oxford, 1699. Master at Sir Joseph Williamson's Mathematical School, Rochester; subsequently came to Cambridge and taught mathematics at Sidney. Became a member of Emmanuel College; M.A. (*Com.Reg.*) 1728. Lucasian Professor of Mathematics 1739-60, and the first Taylor Lecturer at Sidney during the same period. F.R.S. 1713. [*D.N.B.*; *Venn*, I.i, 371]

152 Painter unknown, copy after JOHN WOLLASTON of 1741

$30\frac{1}{8} \times 24\frac{3}{4}$ in. (76.5 × 62.9 cm.). Canvas. Half-length, to left. White wig. Wears black academical gown with black scarf and bands. Within a painted oval.

Source of acquisition unknown. First recorded in the Master's inventory (William Chafy) of 1813.

The original by Wollaston, signed and dated 1741, is in the Old Schools.[a] This copy is perhaps of the eighteenth century.

NOTE. (a) *Goodison*, p. 26, no. 29.

CROMWELL, OLIVER

1599-1658. Fellow-Commoner 1616-17. Lord Protector of the Commonwealth of England, Scotland and Ireland, 1653-8. [*D.N.B.*; *Venn*, I.i, 423; biographies by C. Hill (1970) and A. Fraser (1973)]

153 After SIR PETER LELY   PLATE VI

$29\frac{1}{8} \times 24\frac{1}{8}$ in. (74.0 × 61.3 cm.). Canvas. Half-length, front, the head turned slightly to the right. He wears armour, with a plain, turned down white collar. Within a painted, sculptured oval.

Given by T. Knox-Shaw, academic year 1934-5. (?) Coll. Richard Cromwell, the Protector's third son (1626-1712) and his successor as Lord Protector; said to have been in the possession of the Sandeman family of Ware, Hertfordshire, about 1914; coll. William Barber of Peterborough; acquired by a Peterborough dealer, B. Laxton, from whom it was bought by the donor.

This portrait, which appears to be of the late seventeenth or early eighteenth century, follows a well-known portrait-pattern of Cromwell, of which the best version, signed by Sir Peter Lely, is in the Birmingham Art Gallery (no. P.27'49). The Lely pattern, which became to some extent an official image, is closely connected with the portrait miniature by Samuel Cooper belonging to the Duke of Buccleuch, from which it may well derive. This miniature, of which there are many versions and variations, is believed to be from the life, and is considered to be perhaps of 1653, when Cromwell was installed as Lord Protector; a repetition of it by Cooper in the National Portrait Gallery (no. 3065) is signed and dated 1656. The Lely pattern is thought to have probably originated in 1653 or 1654; a mezzotint of it by J. Faber jun., of 1735, is inscribed 'Petrus Lely pinx 1653'.[a] An inscription, now obliterated, recorded as on the back of the canvas, stated that the portrait formerly belonged to Richard Cromwell.

NOTE. (a) See David Piper, 'The contemporary portraits of Oliver Cromwell', *Walpole Society*, xxxiv (1958), 31ff, 39–40, no. 5, pl. IXA.

154 Painter unknown, after SAMUEL COOPER, (?) 19th century

$8\frac{5}{8} \times 7$ in. (21.9 × 17.8 cm.). (?) Canvas;[a] in an oval mount. Bust, in profile left. Wears armour, with a white falling band. Green background.

Given by A. C. Benson, 1904.

This resembles in reverse a drawing in the Devonshire collection at Chatsworth, by or after Samuel Cooper (1609-1672). Being in reverse, it is probably taken from an engraving of the drawing, either J. Houbraken's of 1747, or a later example.

NOTE. (a) As the back is covered over, it cannot be ascertained whether this is on canvas or wood.

155 Painter unknown, 17th century, probably after SIR PETER LELY

$13\frac{5}{8} \times 11\frac{5}{8}$ in. (34.6 × 28.9 cm.). Pastel. Head, slightly to right. Brown hair falling in ringlets almost to the shoulders; tuft on lower lip. Wears brown armour, with white falling collar.

Given by Thomas Hollis, 1766.

Formerly considered to be the work of Samuel Cooper (1609-1672), but this view is no longer generally accepted;[a] in rather rubbed condition as it is, and therefore not easy to judge, it seems in style to be decidedly below the quality of Cooper. Furthermore, it relates directly in the character of the head to the portrait-pattern of Lely's oil paintings of Cromwell, which, though based on Cooper, differ noticeably from his miniatures, most strikingly in the elongated proportions of the face.[b] See above no. **153**. Another version of this pastel, slightly larger in size, very close to it but inferior in quality, belongs to Mr. R. R. Parker at Browsholme Hall, Lancashire. In the

National Portrait Gallery is a copy of no. **155** by Robert Hutchinson (no. 2426), made in 1773.

ENGRAVED and REPRODUCED. A list is given in Wilbur Cortez Abbott, *A bibliography of Oliver Cromwell* (Harvard, 1929), p. 384, to which may be added a reproduction in J. J. Foster's *Samuel Cooper* (1914–16), pl. XXX, opp. p. 28.

NOTES. (a) David Piper, 'The contemporary portraits of Oliver Cromwell', *Walpole Society*, xxxiv (1958), 39, no. 4; *Catalogue of seventeenth-century portraits in the National Portrait Gallery* (1963), p. 93, no. 2426. (b) *Ibid.*; Oliver Millar, *Sir Peter Lely* (National Portrait Gallery, 1978), p. 47.

EMELÉUS, HARRY JULIUS

Born 1903. Fellow 1945. Staff of Imperial College, London, 1931–45; Professor of Inorganic Chemistry, University of Cambridge, 1945–70. D.Sc. (London). Honorary degrees from several universities. C.B.E. 1958; F.R.S. 1946. Author, scientific.

156 By MARGARET FEREMAN, 1984

$25\frac{1}{2} \times 19\frac{1}{2}$ in. (64.8 × 49.5 cm.). Pencil on white paper. Half-length, seated, to front; right leg crossed over left, right hand in lap, left elbow on arm of chair, hand up to cheek. Bare-headed, clean-shaven. Wears jacket over cardigan, and trousers. Knotted tie.

Commissioned by the College.

FISHER, BARDSEY

c. 1657–1723. Admitted pensioner 1674; B.A. 1677–8; M.A. 1681; D.D. 1704. Rector of Newmarket (St. Mary's) 1694. Master 1704–23. Vice-Chancellor 1705–6. [*Venn*, I.ii, 142]

157 By JOHN VERELST   PLATE VIII

$49 \times 39\frac{1}{2}$ in. (124.5 × 103 cm.). Canvas. To knees, seated in a high-backed chair. Wears scarlet D.D. gown, with black scarf and bands. Signed top left 'Jo: Verelst. P', and inscribed top right, 'Acad: Cantab: procan./A.D. 1706'.

Source of acquisition unknown, but before about 1790 (see below).

Together with the following portrait of his wife, unrecorded in the inventories taken by successive Masters until that of William Chafy in 1813, and then only doubtfully identified. But already in about 1790 listed by *Masters* among the portraits in the College with the names of Bardsey Fisher and his wife.[a] As Fisher died intestate, it has been surmised that if the portraits were left in the Master's Lodge at his death, as seems at least possible, this could have led to doubts about their true ownership, causing the omission from the periodical inventories. Although undated, there can be little doubt that this portrait, like the dated companion picture of Mrs. Fisher, no. **158**, was painted in 1706, at the period of Fisher's Vice-Chancellorship.

NOTE. (a) Page 27, nos. 7 and 8.

FISHER, MRS. BARDSEY
Born Elizabeth Flesher. Married Bardsey Fisher, 1694.

158 By JOHN VERELST, 1706
$49 \times 36\frac{3}{4}$ in. (124.5×93.3 cm.). Canvas. To knees, turned front, leaning to her left. Wears grey décolleté dress. Landscape background to left. Signed and dated at right, 'Jno. Verelst/P:1706'.

Source of acquisition unknown, but before about 1790 (see no. **157**).

Companion portrait to that of her husband above. It seems at least likely, in view of the date 1706 on this portrait, and the inscription on Dr. Fisher's, that the pair were painted to mark his Vice-Chancellorship during the academical year 1705-6.

GARNETT, JOHN
1709-1782. Admitted pensioner at St. John's College, 1725; migrated to Sidney, 1728; scholar; B.A. 1728-9; M.A. 1732; B.D. 1739; D.D. (*Lit.Reg.*) 1752. Fellow, 1730. Chaplain to the Lord-Lieutenant of Ireland, 1751; Bishop of Ferns, 1752-8, and of Clogher, 1758-82. Author, theological. [*D.N.B.*; *Venn*, I.ii, 196]

159 Painter unknown
$25 \times 20\frac{1}{2}$ in. (63.5×52.1 cm.). Canvas. Half-length, half to right. Bushy white wig. Wears episcopal rochet and chimere. A mitre to right.

Source of acquisition unknown. First recorded in the Master's inventory (William Elliston) of 1760.

Since he is depicted in episcopal dress, this cannot be before 1752 when he became Bishop of Ferns.

GREEN, HOWARD LESLIE HAYDON HAVELOCK
1899-1984. Admitted pensioner, 1919; subsequently scholar; B.A. 1922; M.A. 1926; B.Chir., M.D. 1936; Raymond Horton-Smith Prizeman, 1937. Research Fellow, 1925; Fellow, 1927; Taylor Lecturer, 1927-64; University Lecturer in Anatomy, 1933-64.

160 By JOHN EDWARDS
$18 \times 13\frac{5}{8}$ in. (45.7×35.7 cm.). Black chalk on white paper. Nearly half-length seated, somewhat to right, right arm on arm of chair. Bare-headed, clean-shaven, with spectacles. Behind the head, the back of an upholstered chair. Signed lower right, 'John Edwards'.

Commissioned by his former medical students, 1980.

A good likeness.

GRIFFITHS, ERNEST HOWARD
1851-1932. Admitted sizar, 1870; B.A. 1874; M.A. 1877; Sc.D. 1902. Fellow, 1897-1903; Honorary Fellow, 1904-32. Principal and Professor

of Experimental Philosophy, University College, Cardiff, 1901–18; Vice-Chancellor, University of Wales, 1903–5, 1909–11 and 1915–17. D.Sc. Wales; Hon. LL.D. Aberdeen; Hon. D.Sc. Victoria and Liverpool. F.R.S. 1895. Author, scientific. [*D.N.B. 1931–1940; Venn*, II.iii, 155]

161 By M. LINDSAY WILLIAMS, 1908
$23\frac{1}{2} \times 19\frac{1}{2}$ in. (59.7 × 49.5 cm.). Canvas. Bust, front. Bald, grey hair, beard and moustache. Wears dark grey suit with white collar and knotted tie. Signed and dated lower right, 'M. Lindsay Williams 1908'.

Source of acquisition unknown. First recorded in the Master's inventory (G. A. Weekes) of 1918.

HEY, JOHN

1734–1815. Admitted pensioner at St. Catharine's College, 1750–1. B.A. 1755; M.A. 1758; B.D. 1765; D.D. 1780. Fellow of Sidney, 1758–79; Tutor, 1760–79. Norrisian Professor of Divinity, 1780–95. Author, theological. [*D.N.B.; Venn*, I.ii, 363]

162 Painter unknown
$29\frac{1}{2} \times 24\frac{3}{8}$ in. (74.9 × 61.9 cm.). Canvas. Bust, front. Close, bushy wig. Wears black clothes with a white cravat.

Source of acquisition unknown. First recorded in the Master's inventory (F. J. H. Wollaston) of 1807.

JOHNSON, JAMES

1633–1704. Admitted pensioner, 1655; B.A. 1658–9; M.A. 1662; B.D. 1669; D.D. 1689. Fellow, 1662–88. Master, 1688–1704. Vice-Chancellor, 1689–90. Benefactor. [*Venn*, I.ii, 478]

163 By VALENTINE RITZ, 1690, after JACOB HOUSEMAN (or HUYSMANS)
$29\frac{1}{4} \times 24\frac{1}{2}$ in. (74.3 × 62.2 cm.). Canvas. Half-length, front. Dark hair. Wears black academical gown and scarf, with bands. Above a red table holds in his left hand a partly unrolled scroll, inscribed '. . . houseman/nach dem leben/ cop:/by V. Ritz', and dated below '1690'; above the inscription a line of illegible words.

Source of acquisition unknown. First recorded in the Master's inventory (Joseph Craven) of 1723.

Jacob Houseman or Huysmans (1633?–1696) came to England *c.*1660; he lived in London. Valentine Ritz was resident in Cambridge, where he is known to have painted portraits, restored pictures and carried out decorative work. He was active into the earlier eighteenth century.

164 Painter unknown, copy after VALENTINE RITZ
$25\frac{5}{8} \times 24\frac{1}{2}$ in. (65.1 × 62.2 cm.). Canvas. Bust length, within a painted oval. Copy of no. **163**.

Source of acquisition unknown. First recorded as above.

KNOX-SHAW, THOMAS

1886–1972. Admitted scholar, 1905; B.A. (4th Wrangler) 1908; M.A. 1912. Fellow, 1909–45; College Lecturer, 1914; Tutor, 1919–29. University Lecturer in Mathematics, 1926–9; University Treasurer, 1929–45. Master, 1945–57. M.C. 1916 and Belgian Croix de Guerre. C.B.E. 1954; Hon. A.R.I.B.A. Benefactor. [*Who's Who*]

165 By SIR JAMES GUNN, R.A., 1949   PLATE XI

29 × 24¾ in. (73.7 × 61.9 cm.). Canvas. Half-length, front. Greying hair. His hands clasped before him. Wears black academical gown over dark grey suit; white shirt collar. In the background to left, a draped green curtain. Signed lower right, 'James Gunn'.

Commissioned by the College, 1949.

LINNETT, JOHN WILFRID

1913–1975. Admitted at St. John's College, Oxford, 1931; B.A. 1934; M.A. 1938; D.Phil. 1938. Henry Fellow, Harvard University, 1937–8. Junior Research Fellow, Balliol College, 1939–45; Fellow of Queen's College, 1945–65. University Demonstrator in Chemistry, 1944–62, and Reader in Inorganic Chemistry, 1962–5, at Oxford. Professor of Physical Chemistry at Cambridge, 1965–75. Fellow of Emmanuel College, 1965–70. Master of Sidney, 1970–5. Vice-Chancellor, 1973–5. Honorary Fellow of St. John's College, Oxford, 1968–75, and of Queen's College, Oxford, 1971–5. F.R.S. 1955. Author, scientific. [*Who's Who*]

166 By W. E. NARRAWAY, 1978

43½ × 29⅛ in. (110.5 × 74.0 cm.). Canvas. Three-quarter length, standing, to front. Grey hair. His hands clasped before him. Wears black cassock with bands. Signed and dated lower right. 'Narraway 78'.

Commissioned by the College, 1978.

Posthumous portrait, painted from photographs. He is attired as Vice-Chancellor of the University.

McCANCE, ROBERT ALEXANDER

Born 1898. Admitted pensioner, 1919; subsequently scholar; B.A. 1922; M.A. 1926; Ph.D. 1926; M.D. 1929. Fellow, 1938. University Reader in Medicine, 1938–45; Professor of Experimental Medicine, 1945–66. C.B.E. 1953; F.R.S. 1948; F.R.C.P. 1935. Author of works on mineral metabolism, the chemical composition of foods and the physiology of the newborn animal. [*Who's Who*]

167 By W. E. NARRAWAY, 1979

28¾ × 26¾ in. (73.0 × 67.9 cm.). Pencil on white paper. Half-length seated, half right, left hand in lap, right hand on table left. Bare-headed, clean-shaven, with spectacles. Wears jacket with zip fastener over jersey. On table a copy of a Medical Research Council volume, *Special Report Series No. 297. The Composition of Foods*, by R. A. McCance and E. M. Widdowson. Signed and dated lower right, 'Narraway 79'.

Commissioned by the Neonatal Society, 1979.

Commissioned to mark his eightieth birthday. A good likeness.

MACHRAY, ROBERT

1831–1904. Admitted pensioner, 1851; later scholar; B.A. 1855; M.A. 1858; D.D. 1865. Fellow, Dean, 1858. Vicar of Madingley (Cambs.), 1862–5. Bishop of Rupert's Land, 1865–93; Archbishop of Rupert's Land and Primate of All Canada, 1893–1904. Chancellor, University of Manitoba, 1877. Hon. D.D. Oxford, Durham and Manitoba; Hon. D.C.L. Toronto. Prelate of the Order of St. Michael and St. George, 1893. [*D.N.B. 1901–11; Venn*, II.iv, 267]

168 By W. S. SUTTON

$29\frac{1}{8} \times 24\frac{1}{4}$ in. (74.0 × 61.6 cm.). Canvas. Half-length, front. White hair and beard. Wears episcopal rochet and chimere, with black scarf. On a blue and red ribbon round his neck wears the badge of the Prelate of the Order of St. Michael and St. George. Signed lower left, 'W. S. Sutton'.

Given by his nephew, J. A. Machray, of Winnipeg, 1914.

This must date no earlier than 1893, when he became Prelate of the Order of St. Michael and St. George.

MATTHEWS, EDMUND

c. 1615–1692. Admitted sizar, 1632; B.A. 1636–7; M.A. 1640; B.D. 1647. Fellow, 1641–92 under Charles I, the Commonwealth and the Protectorate, Charles II, James II, and William and Mary. [*Venn*, I.iii, 161]

169 Painter unknown, 1653

$29\frac{1}{2} \times 24\frac{3}{8}$ in. (74.9 × 61.9 cm.). Canvas. Half-length, slightly to the right. Black skull-cap over shoulder-length dark hair; fair moustache and lower lip tuft. Wears black academical gown over black dress, with a plain falling band open at the front, with tassels, and white pleated cuffs. On a green-covered table at the right stand several books, one of them, which he touches with his right hand, the Septuagint, open at the 124th Psalm. Upper right, a tablet inscribed 'Anno $\frac{\overline{\text{Dni}} \ 1653}{\text{Aetatis } 36}$ '.

Bequeathed by Edward ffarington Matthews, 1934.

If the date in the inscription is accepted as correct, it becomes apparent that Matthews must have been in his 37th or 38th year, rather than in his 36th, since he was baptised in July 1616. Though in appearance he looks remarkably young to be of this age, the form of collar and cuffs accord satisfactorily with the date of 1653. In this year, when the Barebone's Parliament met in July, it was believed that among the measures contemplated was the suppression of the universities and their colleges. The removal of this expected threat by a sudden dissolution in December was interpreted as an act of divine intervention, hence possibly the reference to the 124th Psalm.

MONTAGU of Boughton, EDWARD MONTAGU, first Baron

1562-1644. Great-nephew of the Foundress. Matriculated from Christ Church, Oxford, c.1574; B.A. 1579. K.B. at the coronation of James I, 1603; created Baron Montagu of Boughton, 1621. M.P. for Brackley, 1601, and subsequently for Northamptonshire. Lord Lieutenant of Northamptonshire, arrested by order of the Parliament because of his known loyalty to the King, 1642, and died a prisoner. Benefactor. [*D.N.B.*]

170 Painter unknown

$28\frac{3}{4} \times 23\frac{1}{2}$ in. (73.1 × 59.7 cm.). Canvas. Half-length, turned half right. Fair hair, beard and moustache. Wears red and white baron's parliament robes; the badge of the Order of the Bath hangs on the red ribbon of the Order round his neck, he grasps the ribbon with his right hand; the right sleeve is white, with a lace-edged cuff. Top right, within a square, his arms, which were quarterly argent and or, three fusils gules, within a bordure sable (for Montagu), an eagle vert (for Monthermer); crest, head of a gryphon or with wings sable; supporters two gryphons or with wings sable; motto ÆQVITAS ACTIONVM REGVLA.[a] Within a painted oval.

Source of acquisition unknown. First recorded in the Master's inventory (Samuel Ward) of 1639.

The arms with supporters are those of a peer and the portrait thus dates at the earliest from 1621 when he was created a baron. It is of note that it came to the College during his lifetime.

NOTE. (a) The heraldry as painted defines this blazon very inadequately.

MONTAGU (or MONTAGUE), JAMES

c.1568-1618. Great-nephew of the Foundress. Matriculated Fellow-Commoner from Christ's College, 1585; D.D. (by special Grace), 1598. The first Master of Sidney, 1596-1608, Dean of Lichfield, 1603-4, and of Worcester, 1604-8; Bishop of Bath and Wells, 1608-16, and of Winchester, 1616-18. Edited the works of James I and translated them into Latin. Benefactor. [*D.N.B.*; *Peile*, i, 161; *Venn*, I.iii, 201]

171 Painter unknown

$28\frac{1}{2} \times 23\frac{7}{8}$ in. (72.4 × 60.7 cm.). Canvas. Half-length, slightly right. Brown beard and moustache. Wears square, soft black cap, and episcopal rochet and chimere, with white arching collar. Upper right, his arms, encircled by the Garter, argent, three fusils gules, impaling those of the see of Winchester, gules, two keys addorsed in bend, one argent the other or, a sword interposed between them in bend sinister of the second. Within a painted oval.

Source of acquisition unknown. First recorded in the Master's inventory (Samuel Ward) of 1639.

The Prelate of the Order of the Garter is always the Bishop of Winchester, hence the form of the arms. Thus the portrait, in this form, dates at the earliest from 1616; a three-quarter length version, seated, with the quartered arms of Montagu and Monthermer (see above, no. **170**) but not encircled by the Garter, and thus before 1616, was in the Captain F. Montagu sale at Christie's, 28 June 1946 (89). An example of the present portrait, probably a copy, is in the Bishop's Palace at Wells.

MONTAGU, SIR WILLIAM

*c.*1619–1706. Admitted Fellow-Commoner, 1632. M.P. for Huntingdon, 1640, for the University, 1660, and for Stamford, 1661–76. Attorney-General to the Queen, 1662–76; Chief Baron of the Exchequer, 1676–86; removed from the bench for refusing to give an unqualified opinion in favour of the prerogative of dispensation, 1686. [*D.N.B.*; *Venn*, I.iii, 202]

172 School of DANIEL MYTENS, 1639   PLATE III

82 × 49 in. (208.3 × 124.5 cm.). Canvas. Whole-length, standing, slightly to right. Holds a staff in his right hand with a brown glove, left hand on his hip, holding a glove. Light brown hair to shoulders, fair moustache and lower lip tuft. Wears a warm grey silk doublet, braided and slashed down the insides of the sleeves; a white collar edged with lace scallops covers the shoulders, cuffs with similar lace edging. Braided brown trunks terminating in a double row of loops of ribbon; white boots with wide, braided tops, high red heels and spurs. He stands on a brown, chequered pavement; to right a balustrade, with a distant landscape beyond, to left a brownish pink curtain the full height of the picture. On the toe of his right boot an almost erased inscription.[a]

Coll. J. E. Rawlins, Syston Court, Gloucestershire, sold 21–24 May 1935 (139) by Norfolk Prior, bt. David Minlore; bt. from him by the College, 1935.[b]

When cleaned and restored in 1976 the removal of overpaint covering almost the whole picture revealed many damages and some alterations; in particular most of the face was the work of restorers, and in common with much of the rest of the picture the original paint is now very thin. A biographical inscription, lower left, on top of overpaint, was removed with it. At this time the date 1639 in front of his right boot was just decipherable,[c] but is so no longer. At the Syston Court sale the picture was catalogued as by Daniel Mytens, together with a companion portrait of Sir William Montagu's sister, Frances Countess of Rutland. On grounds of the apparent age of the sitter, the date of 1639 may be accepted, but an attribution to Mytens is then out of the question, as by 1637 he was living in the Hague, and seems to have quitted England by 1634, when Sir William Montagu was about fifteen. But the picture is certainly of the circle of Mytens. It is of the general type of his full-length portraits of men, and in particular is very similar in design, pose and dress to a portrait of the first Duke of Hamilton (Duke of Hamilton and Brandon), signed, and dated 1629, though the costume is perfectly possible for 1639. The Hamilton portrait was a work of exceptional distinction at its date, evidently leading to the perpetuation of its design among painters working in the Mytens tradition.

NOTES. (a) What little can be deciphered shows it to have been biographical; as it refers to him as Chief Baron Montagu it must date from after 1676 when he became Lord Chief Baron of the Exchequer. (b) In 1651 Syston Court became the property of Samuel Trotman, whose son Samuel married Elizabeth Montagu, daughter of Sir William, as his second wife. The house passed by descent to Major Fiennes Dickenson, who sold it, together with the portraits and other paintings, in 1903 to James Henry Rawlins. It is an obvious deduction that the portrait entered the possession of the Trotman family through Elizabeth Montagu. (c) Report of the restorer, Miss F. V. Emeléus, together with the details of condition.

NEVILLE, FRANCIS HENRY

1847-1915. Admitted pensioner, 1867; B.A. 1871; M.A. 1874. Fellow, 1871-1915; College Lecturer in Chemistry and Physics. F.R.S. 1897. Author, scientific, in the field of metallurgy. [*Venn*, II.iv, 528]

173 By CHARLES HASLEWOOD SHANNON, R.A., 1914

$32\frac{1}{2} \times 27\frac{1}{4}$ in. (82.5 × 69.2 cm.). Canvas. Half-length, seated, front. Dark hair, grey beard and moustache. Wears black academical gown over grey clothes; dark knotted tie. Signed and dated lower right, 'Charles Shannon 1914'.

Commissioned from a fund subscribed by his friends and pupils, and acquired in the academic year 1914-15.

174 By W. HAMMOND SMITH, 1912

$23\frac{1}{2} \times 19\frac{1}{2}$ in. (59.7 × 49.5 cm.). Canvas. Half length, turned half left. Dark hair, grey beard and moustache. Wears dark clothes; grey-green knotted tie. Signed and dated 'WHS/1912'.

Given by the artist, 1916.

NORTHCOTE, DONALD HENRY

Born 1921. B.Sc. (London) 1944; Ph.D. (London) 1948. Admitted Downing College, 1948; M.A. 1949; Sc.D. 1964. Fellow of St. John's College, 1960-76; Master of Sidney, 1976. University Demonstrator in Biochemistry, 1948-53; University Lecturer, 1953-65; Reader in Plant Biochemistry, 1965-72; Professor of Plant Biochemistry, 1972. Honorary Fellow of Downing College, 1977. F.R.S. 1968. Author, scientific.

175 By MICHAEL NOAKES, 1983

$28\frac{3}{8} \times 24\frac{3}{8}$ in. (72.1 × 61.9 cm.). Canvas. Half-length, seated, hands clasped in lap, right leg crossed over left. Bare-headed, clean-shaven. Wears grey suit, a red knotted tie. Grey background. Signed and dated lower right, 'Michael Noakes/1983'.

Commissioned by the College, 1983.

A good likeness.

PERKINS, WILLIAM

1558–1602. Matriculated pensioner from Christ's College, 1577; B.A. 1580–1; M.A. 1584. Fellow of Christ's, 1584–95; lecturer at Great St. Andrew's, Cambridge, until 1602. A notable teacher and theological writer of strong Calvinist opinions whose works were translated into Dutch, Spanish, Irish and Welsh. James Montagu (no. **171**) preached the sermon at his funeral and was an executor of his will, and Samuel Ward (no. **189**) admired him greatly. [*D.N.B.; Peile*, i, 141; *Venn*, I.iii, 347; *N.C.B.E.L.*, i, 1931–2]

176 Painter unknown

$22\frac{3}{4} \times 20$ in. (57.8 × 50.8 cm.). Wood. Bust, slightly to left. Holds before him in both hands an open brown book, the right hand deformed, with no thumb and only one finger. Receding, reddish fair hair, reddish beard and moustache. Wears black gown over black doublet, with narrow white ruff.

Source of acquisition unknown. First recorded in the Master's inventory (Samuel Ward) of 1639.

Much rubbed and abraded; probably of the fairly early seventeenth century. A smaller version is at Christ's College (above, no. **66**). A number of engraved portraits of Perkins, such as that in Henry Holland's *Herωologia Anglica*, 1620, p. 219, are similar to this portrait, but with the difference of showing the left hand slightly raised in an expository gesture.

ENGRAVED. Line-engraving by Simon van de Passe.[a]

NOTE. (a) D. Franken, *L'oeuvre gravé des van de Passe* (1881), p. 150, no. 816.

PHELPS, ROBERT

1808–1890. Brother of the actor Samuel Phelps. Admitted sizar at Trinity College, 1828; later scholar; B.A. 1833; M.A. 1836; B.D. 1843; Hon. D.D. 1843 (on the occasion of Queen Victoria's visit). Migrated to Sidney where he became Taylor Lecturer in 1836, Fellow, 1838 and Tutor in 1840. Master, 1843–90. Vice-Chancellor, 1844–5 and 1847–8. Rector of Willingham, 1848–90. Led opposition to reforms proposed by the University Commissioners. [*Venn*, II.v, 105]

177 By A. E. EMSLIE, 1890

$43\frac{3}{8} \times 33\frac{3}{8}$ in. (110.2 × 84.7 cm.). Canvas. Half-length seated, to front, his hands on his knees. Wears scarlet D.D. gown with black scarf, over black clothes. Signed and dated lower right, 'A. E. Emslie/1890'.

Source of acquisition unknown.

Left unfinished by the painter, presumably because the sittings were incomplete at the time of Phelps's death on 11 January 1890. Finished subsequently by Miss F. V. Emeléus in 1976. The only record of the portrait is in the list of those in the College given in *Atkinson and Clark*, p. 469.

ROBINSON, SIR EDWARD AUSTIN GOSSAGE

Born 1897. Admitted scholar, Christ's College, 1919; B.A. 1921; M.A. 1925. Fellow of Corpus Christi College, 1923–26 and of Sidney, 1931. University Lecturer in Economics, 1929–50; Professor of Economics, 1950–65. Knight bachelor, 1975; C.M.G. 1947; O.B.E. 1944; F.B.A. 1955. Author of numerous works on economics, notably on problems in economic development.

178   By ROBERT TOLLAST

20 × 13¼ in. (50.8 × 33.7 cm.). Red, white and black chalk on buff paper. Half-length, slightly to left. Bare-headed, clean-shaven. Wears suit with pullover. Signed lower left, 'R. Tollast'.

Commissioned by the College Investments Committee and Lazard Brothers & Co. Ltd., 1978.

Commissioned to mark his eightieth birthday.

SMAIL, RAYMOND CHARLES

Born 1913. Admitted exhibitioner, 1932; B.A. 1935; M.A. 1939; Ph.D. 1948. Research Fellow, 1938–46. Fellow, 1946; Tutor, 1946–53; Senior Tutor, 1953–6. University Lecturer in History, 1948–80. M.B.E. 1945. F.S.A. Historian of the Crusades.

179   By JOHN WARD, 1980

18⅛ × 12 in. (46.3 × 30.5 cm.). On brown paper, lights and shadows picked out in white and brown body colour and water colour, slight colour in head and hands. Three-quarter length seated, to knees, half to right, elbows on arms of chair, hands clasped before him. Bare-headed, clean-shaven. Wears jacket and trousers. Behind the figure, shelves of old, large volumes. Signed and dated lower left, 'John Ward 1980'.

Commissioned by students of Confraternitas Historica, 1980.

He is depicted as College Archivist, in the Muniment Room.

SMITH, CHARLES

1844–1916. Son of Henry Smith, cobbler, of Huntingdon. Admitted pensioner, 1864; B.A. (3rd Wrangler), 1868; M.A. 1871. Fellow, 1868–90; Tutor, 1875–90; Master, 1890–1916. An able mathematical teacher and a reformative master. Vice-Chancellor, 1895–7. Author, mathematical. Father of W. Hammond Smith who painted this portrait and no. **174**. [*Venn*, II.v, 543]

180   By W. HAMMOND SMITH

19 × 22 in. (48.2 × 55.9 cm.). Canvas. Short half-length, to front. White hair, beard and moustache. Wears black clothes and academical gown, with a white collar and knotted tie.

Given by Mrs. Charles Smith, academical year 1916–17.

SUSSEX, LADY FRANCES SIDNEY, Countess of

1531–1589. The Foundress of the College by her will of 1588. Fourth daughter of Sir William Sidney, Chamberlain and Steward of the Household to Edward VI; aunt of Sir Philip Sidney. Married to Thomas Radcliffe (no. 185), Viscount Fitzwalter, subsequently Earl of Sussex, 1555.

181   Attributed to STEVEN VAN DER MEULEN, *circa* 1565   FRONTISPIECE
$76 \times 43\frac{3}{4}$ in. (193.0 × 111.1 cm.). Wood. Whole-length standing, slightly to left, her right hand on the arm of a chair behind her, her left holding a brown fur 'flea cravat' with a carved and jewelled animal's head; on the floor beside her, to left, a small dog. Fair hair, with a jewelled cap at the back of the head. She wears a black furred gown, richly ornamented with jewels, over a black dress similarly ornamented, with a light blue, black-edged ruff enriched with pearls, and similar cuffs. Under the gown is a jewelled collar with a pendant pearl, and a jewelled chain hangs from the waist ending at the base of the skirt in a pomander. Across the arms of the chair rests a richly embroidered cushion. Behind the chair, at either side, hangs a draped pink curtain, with the scallops of a canopy above. On the floor is a patterned oriental carpet.

First recorded in the Master's inventory (Samuel Ward) of 1639. Probably came through her executors on the foundation of Sidney Sussex College in 1596 under the terms of her will.

Steven van der Meulen (*fl.*1543–68) was an Antwerp painter, who was living in London in 1560; no work can be attributed to him after 1568. The portrait was first attributed to him in 1969;[a] it can be dated from the costume *circa* 1565. The rather unusual proportion of figure to picture space suggests that it may have been cut down on all four sides. It is regarded as the painter's 'most spectacular portrait'.[b] A half-length portrait of the husband of Lady Frances Sidney, Thomas Radcliffe, Earl of Sussex, which may derive from an original by van der Meulen, was in an anonymous sale at Christie's, 4 October 1946 (104). Under the conditions of hygiene at the date of this portrait, vermin were part of daily life. The 'flea cravat' or 'flea tippit' (presumably, from the names, worn round the neck), was a fashionably essential part of the rich costume of noble ladies. They were sometimes made in the form of stuffed animals, mainly in martenskins or sable, often with richly contrived animal heads, as here. The infesting fleas were periodically shaken out.[c] It may be surmised that the Lady Frances is here depicted in the very grandest height of fashion.

ENGRAVED. Mezzotint by J. Faber sen., 1714.[d]

REPRODUCED. *Walpole Society*, vol. ii (1913), pl. XXIV; C. W. Scott-Giles, *Sidney Sussex College* (1951), frontispiece; *Connoisseur*, cxxxix (1957), 216 (9); Roy Strong, *The English icon* (1969), p. 133, no. 89; *The Elizabethan image*, exhibition catalogue (Tate Gallery, 1970), p. 29, no. 43.

NOTES. (a) Roy Strong, *The English icon* (1969), p. 133, no. 89. (b) *Idem, The Elizabethan image*, exhibition catalogue (Tate Gallery, 1970), p. 29, no. 43. (c) Francis Weiss, 'Bejewelled fur tippets' in *Costume, the journal of the Costume Society* (Victoria and Albert Museum, 1970), no. 4, p. 37; Claude Fregnac, *Jewellery from the Renaissance to Art Nouveau* (1973), p. 24, identifies the fur of the flea cravat as sable (rep. p. 19, fig. 30). (d) J. Chaloner Smith, *British mezzotinto portraits*, Part I (1878), p. 285, no. 34.

182 (?) By GEORGE GOWER, *circa* 1575

$26 \times 21\frac{1}{8}$ in. (66.0 × 53.6 cm.). Wood. Half-length, slightly to left. Reddish hair; at the back of the head a black cap with a jewelled band. Wears a black dress ornamented with many pearls, a square jewel at the bosom; a long heavy necklace of pearls, which she touches with her right hand; white ruff and ruff-like cuffs. To left a window. Upper right in a lozenge, with a coronet above it, the arms of Sidney, or a pheon azure, below it an inscription 'LA CONTESSE DE S. . .'

Source of acquisition uncertain. Probably the half-length portrait recorded in the Master's inventory (Samuel Ward) of 1639. Perhaps to be identified with a portrait of the Foundress bequeathed by Dr. Gabriel Goodman, Dean of Westminster (1529(?)-1601).

From the inscription, evidently cut down at the right, and from comparison with the following portrait, no. **183**, also at the left and along the top. The Sidney arms alone in a lozenge, would normally indicate her status as that of a widow, but at the approximate date indicated by the costume, *circa* 1575, her husband, the third Earl of Sussex, was still alive (d.1583). Dr. Gabriel Goodman bequeathed to Christ's College a portrait of their Foundress, the Lady Margaret Beaufort, but it cannot now be positively identified (see above, p. 34).

183 Painter unknown

$28\frac{1}{2} \times 23\frac{3}{4}$ in. (72.4 × 60.3 cm.). Canvas. Copy of the above portrait, no. **182**, with slight differences of detail. Upper left are the arms of Radcliffe, argent a bend engrailed sable, impaling those of Sidney, with those of Sidney within a lozenge upper right. Below the latter an inscription 'LE CONTESS DE SVSSEX'.

Source of acquisition unknown.

Copy probably of the seventeenth century. Probably the portrait first recorded in the Master's inventory (James Johnson) of 1688.

184 Painter unknown

$29 \times 23\frac{3}{4}$ in. (73.7 × 60.4 cm.). Canvas. Copy of the above portrait no. **183**, with slight differences of detail. No arms or inscription.

Source of acquisition unknown.

A copy of poor quality. Probably that first recorded in the Master's inventory (Bardsey Fisher) of 1704.

SUSSEX, SIR THOMAS RADCLIFFE, third Earl of

1526–1583. Husband of the Foundress. Statesman and soldier. M.A. (on the occasion of Queen Elizabeth's visit), 1564. Active in putting down the rebellion of Sir Thomas Wyatt, 1554. A Commissioner to Spain to treat of Queen Mary's marriage to Philip II, 1554; Ambassador to the Emperor for the projected marriage of Queen Elizabeth to the Archduke Charles, 1568; Commissioner for the proposed marriage of Elizabeth to the Duke of Anjou, 1579. Lord Deputy of Ireland, 1556–8, 1559–60 and again (as Lord Lieutenant), 1560–5. As Lord President and Lord Lieutenant of the North suppressed the rebellion of 1569. K.G. 1557. Privy Councillor, 1570; Lord Chamberlain of the Household, 1572–83. [*D.N.B.*; *Venn*, I.iii, 414]

185 Painter unknown, after an original of *circa* 1565

$11\frac{1}{2} \times 9\frac{9}{16}$ in. (29.2 × 24.2 cm.). Wood. Half-length, slightly to right. Black bonnet, tilted over his left ear, with a pink feather and encircled by a jewelled band with the lesser George of the Garter. Fair moustache and slight beard. Over an orange-yellow doublet, with a narrow ruff open in front, wears a black coat with red sleeves and a brown fur collar, jewels round the shoulders. A gold chain round the neck, grasped by his right hand. Inscribed upper left, 'THOMAS/RATCLIFFE', upper right, 'EARL/of/SUSSEX/1565'.

Purchased 1949. Anon. sale, Christie's, 25 February 1949 (26), bt. for the College.

A much repeated portrait-pattern of the Earl of Sussex, going back to an original of *c.*1565, and for the rest of his life the sole standard portrait. A larger version is in the National Portrait Gallery (312), with different colouring and showing more at the base. The portrait formula is ultimately derived from Sir Antonio Mor.[a] The present example is considered to be a modern forgery.[b]

NOTES. (a) Roy Strong, *Tudor and Jacobean portraits*, National Portrait Gallery catalogue, 1969, pp. 308–310. (b) Attributed to one Ellis, of Rochester. In the Christie sale of 1949 it was catalogued as 'Clouet'.

TATE, JAMES

1771–1843. Admitted sizar, 1789; B.A. 1794; M.A. 1797. Fellow, 1795–6. Master of Richmond Grammar School (Yorks.), 1796–1833. Canon Residentiary and Prebendary of St. Paul's, 1833–43. Famous as a classical scholar. [*D.N.B.*; *Venn,* II.vi, 113]

186 By H. W. PICKERSGILL, R.A.

$55\frac{1}{4} \times 43\frac{1}{4}$ in. (140.4 × 109.8 cm.). Canvas. To below the knees, turned half left, seated in a red chair. Wears black clothes, with a white cravat. To right a table, on it a book, *Horatius restitutus*, and papers.

Coll. Rev. James Tate, his grandson (d.1897).[a] Probably entered the possession of the College between 1897 and 1902.[b]

Horatius restitutus, published in 1832, was Tate's chief work of classical scholarship. From an inscription on a mezzotint of the portrait by Samuel

Cousins,[c] dedicated to Earl Grey, it appears that it was painted by subscription among his former pupils as their gift to him, when he left Richmond Grammar School to take up the post of Canon Residentiary of St. Paul's Cathedral, to which he was appointed by the Prime Minister, Earl Grey, in 1833.

NOTES. (a) The portrait was in the possession of the Rev. James Tate at his death, *D.N.B. 1898,* p. 378. (b) The date 1902 can be deduced with reasonable reliability from College records. (c) Alfred Whitman, *Samuel Cousins* (1904), no. 160.

THOMAS, EVAN LEWIS

1858-1935. Admitted pensioner, 1878; later scholar; B.A. 1882; M.A. 1885; LL.M. 1887. Admitted at Lincoln's Inn, 1881; called to the Bar, 1885; Bencher, 1913; Treasurer, 1934. K.C. 1908. Benefactor. [*Venn,* II.vi, 151; *Who's Who*]

187 By ARTHUR MEADE

$24\frac{3}{8} \times 18\frac{1}{2}$ in. (61.9 × 47.0 cm.). Canvas. Bust, front. Wears the long judicial wig of a K.C., with black K.C.'s gown over black dress, lace jabot. Behind, a dark bookcase. Signed lower left, 'Arthur Meade'.

Given by Mrs. Lewis Thomas and Dr. Elwall, 1938.

A good deal of the paint in the face and elsewhere is restoration. Its approximate date may be deduced from its exhibition at the Royal Institute of Oil Painters, London, 1928 (354).

THOMSON, DAVID

1912-1970. Admitted scholar, 1931; B.A. 1934; Gladstone Research Student; Gladstone Memorial Prize, 1937; M.A. 1938; Ph.D. 1938. Research Fellow, 1937-45; Fellow, 1945-57; Senior Tutor, 1945-53; Master of the College, 1957-70. University Lecturer in History, 1948-68; Reader in Modern French History, 1968-70. F.R.Hist.Soc. Author of works on modern English, French and European history.

188 By SIR WILLIAM O. HUTCHISON, P.R.S.A., 1968

$35 \times 27\frac{1}{2}$ in. (88.9 × 69.8 cm.). Canvas. Half-length, seated, to right, his hands clasped in front of him. Grey hair; spectacles. Wears black and scarlet Ph.D. gown. Behind, shelves of books.

Commissioned by the College, 1968.

WARD, SAMUEL

c. 1572-1643. Matriculated pensioner from Christ's College, 1589; B.A. 1592-93; M.A. 1596; B.D. 1603; D.D. 1610. Fellow of Emmanuel College, 1595-1610. Master of Sidney, 1610-43. Vice-Chancellor, 1620-1. Lady Margaret Professor of Divinity, 1623-43. Author, theological; one of the translators of the Authorized Version of the Bible, 1611; Commissioner at the Synod of Dort, 1618. Imprisoned in St. John's College for refusing to contribute to the parliamentary cause, 1643. Benefactor to the College library. [*D.N.B.*; *Peile,* i, 195; *Venn,* I.iv, 334; *N.C.B.E.L.,* i, 1947-8]

189 By VALENTINE RITZ, 1721

$29\frac{1}{2} \times 24\frac{1}{2}$ in. (74.9 × 62.2 cm.). Canvas. Half-length, slightly to right, a book in his right hand, finger between its pages; black skull-cap. Wears black gown over black clothes; white ruff and cuffs.

Source of acquisition unknown.

A portrait of Samuel Ward is first recorded in the Master's inventory (James Johnson) of 1688, which appears to have been the next inventory after Ward's death in 1643. A single portrait of Ward appears in subsequent inventories until that of 1760 (William Elliston), in which two are mentioned, one in the Master's Lodge, and one consigned with others to a garret, where they still seem to have been at the time of the inventory of 1813 (William Chafy). In the catalogue drawn up by Masters is an entry for a single portrait of Ward, which includes the date 1721. As this can have no reference to Ward's career, it can only be surmised that it relates to the date of execution of the portrait, which, on stylistic grounds, can be attributed to Valentine Ritz.[a] In view of these circumstances, it can only be supposed that the original portrait had been damaged or had fallen into disrepair, that this is a copy made of it to preserve Ward's likeness, and that the original was consigned to the garret and lost sight of after the making of the copy in 1721.

NOTE. (a) Cf. the portrait at Christ's College of John Covel (above, no. **14**), a gift from the antiquary William Cole before 1749. Valentine Ritz was a painter resident in Cambridge, where he died in January 1744/5.

WEEKES, GEORGE ARTHUR

1869-1953. Admitted pensioner, 1888; subsequently scholar. B.A. 1891; M.A. 1895. Chaplain of the College, 1893–5; Fellow, 1894–1918; Dean, 1894–1905; Tutor, 1905–18. Master of the College, 1918–45. Vice-Chancellor, 1926–8. Hon. Canon of Ely, 1935. Benefactor. [*Venn*, II.vi, 395]

190 By SIR WALTER W. RUSSELL, R.A.

$35\frac{3}{4} \times 29\frac{1}{2}$ in. (90.7 × 74.9 cm.). Canvas. Half-length, seated, slightly right, holding a paper in his left hand. Wears black cassock and gown, with bands, as Vice-Chancellor. Signed lower left, 'W. Russell'.

Commissioned by the College.[a]

Unfavourably criticised as a likeness when shown at the R.A. in 1928 (101). Another portrait by Sir James Gunn (see below) was commissioned subsequently.

NOTE. (a) Bought from the Master's Portrait Fund, begun in 1927 by subscription among past and present members of the College.

191 By SIR JAMES GUNN, R.A., 1941

$29\frac{1}{2} \times 24\frac{1}{4}$ in. (74.9 × 61.6 cm.). Canvas. Half-length, seated, to left; white hair. Hands clasped before him. Wears dark grey jacket and waistcoat, with clerical collar. Upper left, a draped red curtain. Signed and dated lower right, 'James Gunn 41'.

Commissioned by the College.[a]

Considered to be a 'wonderfully successful' portrait.[b]

NOTES. (a) From the Master's Portrait Fund, see note (a) to no. **190** above. (b) *The Sidney Sussex College Annual* for 1940-41.

WILSON, CHARLES THOMSON REES

1869-1959. B.Sc. (Victoria) 1887. Admitted pensioner, 1888; subsequently scholar; B.A. 1892; Clerk Maxwell Scholar, 1895; M.A. 1897; Hon. Sc.D. 1947. Fellow, 1900-8, 1915-59. University Lecturer in Experimental Physics, 1901-19; Reader in Electrical Meteorology, 1919-25; Jacksonian Professor of Natural Philosophy, 1925-34. Distinguished for his research on condensation nuclei, ions and atmospheric electricity. Nobel Prize (for Physics), 1927. F.R.S. 1900; Copley Medal, 1935. C.H. 1937. Hon. LL.D. Aberdeen and Glasgow; Hon. D.Sc. Manchester, London and Liverpool. [*D.N.B. 1951-60; Venn*, II.vi, 517; *Who's Who*]

192 By SIR JAMES GUNN, R.A.

$29\frac{1}{2} \times 24\frac{1}{2}$ in. (74.9 × 62.2 cm.). Canvas. Half-length, seated, slightly left. Hands clasped, right arm resting on chair back. Bald; greying moustache. Wears dark grey jacket and waistcoat; soft white shirt collar. Behind the figure falls an ochre-yellow curtain. Signed lower right, 'James Gunn'.

Commissioned by the College.

The College Order Book records the appointment on 1 November 1935 of a Committee to have a portrait painted. The label on the frame gives the date of 1936.

WOLLASTON, WILLIAM

1660-1724. Admitted pensioner, 1674; later scholar; B.A. 1678; M.A. 1681. Moral philosopher, celebrated as the author of *The Religion of Nature delineated*, 1722. [*D.N.B.*; *Venn*, I.iv, 447; *N.C.B.E.L.*, ii. 1872]

193 Painter unknown

$28\frac{1}{4} \times 22\frac{3}{4}$ in. (71.7 × 57.8 cm.). Canvas, oval. Short half-length, to right. Periwig. Wears a blue robe, with a loose white cravat.

Given by his grandson,[a] either Francis, heir of William Wollaston's third son Francis, or George, another son of Francis, Fellow of the College (d.1826). In the possession of the College by about 1790.[b]

ENGRAVED. Mezzotint by J. Faber jun.[c]

NOTES. (a) *Atkinson and Clark*, p. 471. (b) *Masters*, p. 27. (c) J. Chaloner Smith, *British mezzotinto portraits*, Part I (1878), p. 447, no. 394.

UNKNOWN MAN, *circa* 1630–40, (?) of the Sidney family

194 Painter unknown

$19\frac{3}{8} \times 13\frac{1}{2}$ in. (49.2 × 34.3 cm.). Wood. Head and shoulders, half right. Auburn hair to shoulders. Wears black doublet, slashed white, with a wide, lace-edged collar.

Source of acquisition unknown. Exh. C.A.S., 1885 (132).

Formerly doubtfully called Sir Philip Sidney (1554–1586), but the date of the costume, *circa* 1630–40, puts this out of the question. The portrait is of a young man, possibly aged 20–25, and thus giving approximate dates of birth between 1605–10 and 1615–20. On these grounds, two of the three sons of Robert Sidney, second Earl of Leicester, are possible candidates, Philip, third Earl (b.1619) and Algernon (b.1622). No portraits of Philip appear to be extant, and those of Algernon have no more than a general resemblance of feature. It is worth a passing thought that Philip, third Earl of Leicester, has possibly been confused in naming the portrait in the past with the more famous Sir Philip Sidney.

UNKNOWN MAN

195 Painter unknown, later 17th century   PLATE VI

$45\frac{1}{4} \times 36\frac{1}{4}$ in. (114.9 × 92.1 cm.). Canvas. Half-length, slightly to right. Dark hair to shoulders. Wears a long buff coat, with a knotted cravat with wide lace ends and a broad black bow; black bows decorate the ends of the sleeves and the cuffs of the shirt; a large black knot is on each shoulder. In his left hand he grasps a backstaff with double quadrant, a defaced inscription on the curved member at its base; holding dividers in his hand he rests his right arm on a globe standing on a table, on which are also a book and a watch.

Source of acquisition unknown. First certainly recorded in the Master's inventory (William Chafy) of 1813.

From style and costume the portrait may be approximately dated to the earlier part of the second half of the seventeenth century.

Believed in the nineteenth century to be a portrait of Ralph Symons, first architect of the College, whose buildings were begun in 1595, but this is ruled out by the date of the painting as well as by the evidence of the prominent scientific attributes.[a] The backstaff with double quadrant was a navigational instrument used for measuring the sun's meridional altitude and thus for establishing the latitude at sea. It was invented by John Davys (1550?–1605), a celebrated navigator and explorer of his time. In the defaced condition of the inscription, all that can now be made out by visual inspection is two virtually illegible words, each beginning with a capital letter, presumably the words of a name, followed by an obscure third word and a clearer date, which is now to be read as 16.8, but has been read in the past both as 1668 and 1698. Examination by infra-red light reveals traces of apparently more than one earlier inscription. Little that is coherent can be made out, but what is revealed of the 'name' corresponds roughly with what can be read visually, followed clearly by the date 1592. A third word does not tally with what can be detected visually, indicating that the latter is contemporary with the repainted 'name'. The first three letters of this 'name' are clearly 'Jon' or 'Joh' and the last letter of the second word is equally clearly 'y' or an abbreviation for 'ng'. The date 1592 is repeated more than once, and infra-red light reveals also the name DAVYS, together with scattered letter forms which include VY. The significance of the association of the name Davys and the date 1592, and of both with the portrait, remains a matter for conjecture. Davys spent the whole of 1592 at sea in an attempt to reach the South Pacific by way of the Straits of Magellan, which he charted. Also in 1592 Emery Molyneux completed his celebrated pair of globes, the terrestrial globe incorporating the discoveries made by Davys in his three voyages to the Arctic, which were commemorated in a Latin inscription upon it.

From examination by infra-red light the date 16.8 is seen to be contemporary with the repainting of the inscription, and thus not indicating the date of the portrait, as has been assumed. Its country of origin is uncertain.

NOTE. (a) That the College had possessed a portrait of Symons is evident from its inclusion in a series of Master's inventories from 1639 to 1746, when it disappears until the inventory of 1813. It was no doubt on the strength of the earlier inclusions that the present portrait was then identified as depicting him. The 1813 inventory by William Chafy lists a 'Portrait – I conceive of Mr. Simons the College Architect', and the next Master's inventory (Robert Phelps) of 1843, makes it clear that this refers to the present portrait.

UNKNOWN MAN

196 Painter unknown, *circa* 1680–90
$28\frac{5}{8} \times 23\frac{5}{8}$ in. (72.7 × 60.0 cm.), oval. Canvas. Nearly half-length, to left. Long, dark periwig. Wears dull pink robe, with a lace cravat.

Source of acquisition unknown.

With some similarity to the work of John Riley (1646–91), but inferior in quality.

CHAPEL ALTARPIECE

PRESEPIO

197 By GIOVANNI BATTISTA PITTONI
$87\frac{1}{2} \times 63$ in. (222.2 × 160.0 cm.). Canvas. At the right, the Virgin Mary, wearing a blue mantle over a red robe, with a white veil over her fair hair, holds the naked Child in her left arm, a white drapery beneath him; she leans or

reclines upon the straw covering a broken wooden framework, at its foot to the right part of a dark grey column. To the left lies the sleeping St. Joseph, with grey hair and beard, in a light blue-grey robe with a golden brown mantle; his left arm, with a white drapery beneath it, rests on the wooden framework, his right arm lies extended beside him; above his head a halo (Mary has none). In the lower left corner are a leathern water-bottle and a short stick. Above Joseph's head are two child angels, one with a scroll, on light grey clouds; above Mary and towards the right, against dark grey clouds, flutter two winged child angel heads.

Acquired for the College in Venice, 1783; received 1784.

Giovanni Battista Pittoni (1687-1767), Venetian School, a founder member of the Venetian Academy and twice its president, was an admired painter of religious and historical subjects. The painting was obtained for the College by the Reverend Thomas Martyn, Professor of Botany in Cambridge and a former Fellow. In September 1781 he wrote to John Strange, British Resident in Venice, who combined with his official duties the activities of a dealer in pictures, asking for his help in finding an altarpiece for Essex's newly completed College chapel.[a] Martyn, who was an amateur of the arts, must have met Strange when on a continental tour of two years, begun in 1778, which included a visit to Venice. In May 1782 Martyn is writing to Strange, evidently in reply to a letter mentioning the possibility of a suitable picture, which, in a letter of September 1782, he refers to as by Pittoni.[b] In a letter of July 1783 Strange writes that he has bought the picture, a 'Presepio', for the sum of 20 guineas, which he considers 'really a trifle'.[c] In August 1784 the picture arrived in England.[d] This frequent theme in Pittoni's work is often treated more or less as here. The only known example on a similar scale is a more elaborate version in the National Gallery (no. 6279), dated to about 1730-40, a good deal later than the present picture, which is placed about 1715-20.[e] A Presepio is a Christmas crib, or, as a subject title for a work of art, the Nativity, though the present composition has sometimes been looked on as a Rest after the Flight into Egypt.[f]

REPRODUCED. *Burlington Magazine*, xlii (1923), 49, and cii (1960), 70.

NOTES. (a) British Library, MS. Egerton 1970. (b) *Ibid.* (c) Sidney Sussex College archives. (d) Sidney Sussex College, library, N.15, *A book of General Receipts and Expenses for Sidney College*, 10 August 1784, 'Paid for the Picture for the Chapel at the Custom House Duty and other charges £5.12.6'. Strange employed as his buyer in Venice Giuseppe Maria Sasso, who may well have obtained this picture for him, though he also had dealings with others. (e) Franca Zara Boccazzi, *Pittoni* (1979), p. 124, no. 41. (f) In March 1784 Martyn, evidently replying to a letter from Strange, asked him if the title he was now giving the picture, 'The Repose in Egypt', was the correct one (*loc. cit.*, note (a)). This subject seems the more likely from the well-grown appearance of the Child. *Masters* refers to both titles, 'The Repose after the Flight into Egypt . . . called by others the Nativity' (p. 27).

PLATE I

LADY MARGARET BEAUFORT,
COUNTESS OF RICHMOND AND DERBY,
painter unknown **(71)**

PLATE II

THOMAS CECIL, first EARL OF EXETER, *painter unknown* (113)

PLATE III

SIR WILLIAM MONTAGU, *school of Daniel Mytens* **(172)**

PLATE IV

ISAAC BARGRAVE
by Cornelius Johnson
(105)

SIR THOMAS BAINES
by Isaac Fuller **(2)**

PLATE V

JOHN MILTON *by Edward Pierce* **(54)**

PLATE VI

OLIVER CROMWELL
after Sir Peter Lely
(153)

UNKNOWN MAN
painter unknown
later 17th century
(195)

PLATE VII

BISHOP JOHN MOORE *by Sir Godfrey Kneller* **(126)**

PLATE VIII

BARDSEY FISHER
by John Verelst **(157)**

LAURENCE ECHARD
by Sir Godfrey Kneller **(23)**

PLATE IX

CHARLES DARWIN
by James Tissot **(16)**

SIR ARTHUR SHIPLEY
by P. A. de László **(85)**

PLATE X

W. L. MOLLISON
by Henry Lamb, R.A.
(124)

G. H. A. WILSON
by Thomas Gunn
(140)

PLATE XI

C. E. RAVEN
by Edmund J. Nelson
(70)

THOMAS KNOX-SHAW
by Sir James Gunn, R.A.
(165)

PLATE XII

SIR HENRY THIRKILL
by Frank Eastman **(132)**

SYDNEY GROSE
by E. X. Kapp **(36)**

INDEX

The subjects covered by the index are as follows: individuals represented and former identifications, artists whose work is represented and former attributions, donors, previous owners. The numbers are those of catalogue entries.

References are to catalogue numbers except where shown otherwise

References are to catalogue numbers except where shown otherwise

References are to catalogue numbers except where shown otherwise